Not ‸ALAN CLARK'S DIARIES

Not ALAN CLARK'S DIARIES

by

PETER BRADSHAW

With an Introduction by Max Hastings
Editor of the *Evening Standard*

POCKET
BOOKS

LONDON • SYDNEY • NEW YORK • TOKYO • SINGAPORE • TORONTO

First published in Great Britain by Pocket Books, 1998
An imprint of Simon & Schuster Ltd
A Viacom Company

Simon & Schuster Ltd.
Africa House
64–78 Kingsway
London
WC2B 6AH

Simon & Schuster Australia
Sydney

A CIP catalogue record for this book is available from the British Library.

ISBN 0-671-02220-2

1 3 5 7 9 10 8 6 4 2

This book is a work of fiction and names, characters,
places and incidents are used fictitiously.

Printed and bound in Great Britain by
Caledonian International Book Manufacturing, Glasgow.

For Alan

CONTENTS

Introduction by Max Hastings   ix

1997   1
1998   127

Appendix: Not Alan Clark's Favourite Things
  Favovourite Women in Politics   187
  Favourite 'Cool Britannia' Styles Icons   189
  Favourite Footballers   191
  Favourite Restaurants   192
  Favourite Cartoon Characters   192
  Favourite Models   193
  Favourite Films   195

Author biography   196

Index   197

INTRODUCTION

Max Hastings

Newspapers seek to entertain and inform. The best parodies do both, because they possess a core of truth. *Private Eye* succeeded brilliantly with 'Mrs Wilson's Diary' and the 'Dear Bill' letters, because each caught a perfect and endearing echo of its alleged author. John Major's *PE* diary was less effective, because the banality of the man inspired banal pastiche.

Soon after I became editor of the *Evening Standard*, I realised that in Peter Bradshaw we possessed a parodist of immense talent. This former academic with his PhD in Eng. Lit and enthusiasm for writing broadcast sitcoms sometimes seemed an odd fish in a mere newspaper office, but also a much-prized one. We set Peter to work producing occasional pastiches of all shapes and sizes, which our readers enjoyed as much as his colleagues. When the 1997 General Election was looming, as we planned our serious coverage I said we would also need a comic diversion. Bradshaw was obviously the man to do it. But what should he do? A few months before, Alan Clark had been adopted as Kensington & Chelsea Tory candidate. On the night of his selection Peter wrote a splendid account of the Conservative meeting in the manner of the Clark *Diaries*. Why not revive that idea, as a regular feature during the Election campaign?

Peter was not wholly sure he wanted to do it, partly because he likes best to write in his own style under his own name. But we cajoled him into action, and the Alan Clark diary became one of the best things in our election coverage. When the campaign ended, I said, 'This is too good to drop.' The hapless Bradshaw was chained to his oar, and the new MP for Kensington & Chelsea became our columnist, whether he liked it or not.

In the beginning, I fancy Alan himself wasn't quite sure whether he was grateful for the publicity, or cross about the tease. During the subsequent legal case, he claimed that we embarked upon the Bradshaw parody in pique, because I had failed to persuade him to write a real column for us.

It was perfectly true that I had offered him a column in the *Evening Standard*, early in 1997. He rang me back to say that he might be interested in doing one, but not for the measly £60,000 or so that I was offering – the *News of the World* were paying him £150,000 for a weekly piece. We would have to come close to that, to be in with a chance.

I was amazed that anybody as rich as Alan cared so much about the money, preferring highly paid bondage at the *NoW* to dignified literary contributions to the *Evening Standard* (that's how we purported to see it, anyway). I wrote back in February:

Dear Alan,

Pamela Harriman [then still above ground] would doff her toupee in admiration for the sums of money you are extracting from the *News of the World*. It is not much good telling a girl she should be honest and virtuous these days, if the rewards of sin are so generous.

Seriously, I would very much like to see you in the *Evening Standard*, but there is no way we could come within a million miles of the sort of money you mention.

One has to gaze at the ceilings of very rich newspaper proprietors indeed, to get that sort of dosh. I don't in the least reproach you for going where the money is, I merely grieve for our readers being deprived of the pleasure of your company in print in the *Evening Standard*.

Yours ever

Alan was mistaken, however, in supposing that there was any linkage between the failure of this dalliance, and the creation of the Bradshaw parody, which he professed to perceive as my revenge – creating our own cheap in-house substitute for the real thing. No, in reality we merely stumbled upon a good joke, and ran with it.

In an age of dreary politicians, Clark is a tonic. An eccentric, an egomaniac, a diarist of genius, he has left a trail of personal and political havoc in his wake for decades. When he was at the Ministry of Defence during the Gulf War, I remember a senior civil servant remarking despairingly, 'We've only got one minister in this place with any brains, and he's mad.'

In his *Diaries*, which wonderfully reveal the chasm between self-perception and reality, Alan supposes himself on the brink of being made Defence Secretary by his adored Margaret. A senior Cabinet Minister of the period claims to have asked Lady Thatcher whether she ever seriously considered appointing him. She replied laconically, 'Would *you* put Alan in charge of a nuclear weapon?'

Clark is a lifelong *enfant terrible*, a man whose favourite pastime is *épater le bourgeois*. When he mused in his *Diaries* about what fun it would be to urinate from his Ministry window on the shuffling masses in the street below, he was evoking a metaphor for his life. An original and entertaining writer of military history, a serial bonker whose

motoring skills would have aroused the admiration of Mr
Toad, his doings filled acres of newsprint even before the
publication of his diaries.

A significant part of the Tory party always loathed him.
They mocked the social pretensions of a man whose
grandfather bought not only his furniture but his own
castle. I remember hearing a Chairman of the backbench
1922 Committee mutter between clenched teeth, 'Don't
people understand that Alan's not *pretending* to be a shit? He
really is one'. But then, Jane Clark said as much about her
husband on television, apparently without derailing marital
harmony.

Alan and I have enjoyed a somewhat tempestuous
relationship over the years. We share a mutual respect for
the German army's performance in the Second World
War, about which both of us have written books. But he
has always thought me intolerably wet politically, and
recounts in his *Diaries* how, in a statemanslike quartet with
John Aspinall, Jimmy Goldsmith and Charles Powell, he
once solicited Conrad Black to lean on me as editor of the
Daily Telegraph for being insufficiently 'on message' about
the glories of Thatcherism.

More recently, I was warmly sympathetic about his
troubles over the Arms to Iraq affair in 1995. It seemed
grotesque that some Tory ministers accused Clark of
conducting a secret trade policy in contravention of official
government policy. Secret? Alan never kept a secret in his
life. He shouted from the rooftops his views about the
absurdities of 'ethical trade'. When he was Trade Minister,
I remember him seizing me like the Ancient Mariner in the
hall of Brooks's club, demanding peremptorily, 'What are
we going to do to stop those idiots in the Foreign Office
trying to prevent us from selling things to the Iraqis, the
only people in the world who actually want to buy them

from us?' Secret policy, my eye.

John Major complained incessantly in private about the trouble Alan Clark had caused him. I once ventured to point out to Mr Major that nobody sane who knew Alan, great entertainer as he is, would have thought of putting him in charge of anything. Having been batty enough to do so, how could one be surprised by what followed? 'It was Margaret who gave him a job,' said the Prime Minister crossly. 'Yes, but you kept him in it.' Silence.

The *Evening Standard*'s satirical version of Clark was by no means the pioneer in the field. A choice parody enjoyed private circulation a few years ago in Tory parliamentary circles. It was read aloud, amid eager applause, to a group of Clark mates and political colleagues. The work of that august figure Sir Alastair Goodlad, MP, it revealed in Goodlad a hitherto unsuspected talent for low comedy. Clark was depicted soliciting some fruity young thing outside St James's, Piccadilly, on his way home from White's, and being irked by her pathetic excuses for turning him down. It ended, as I recall: 'Got back to Albany and rang Jane at Saltwood. Poor darling, she is so tired after cleaning out the moat all day.' I suppose I should have learned something about the limits of the Clark sense of self-mockery, when I heard that he was the one who laughed least convincingly at the reading of the Goodlad pastiche.

In the early days of Peter Bradshaw's Clark Diary, I offered the author a certain amount of guidance about Clark's habits, friends, watering holes, enthusiasms, to add verisimilitude to the tale. I worried a bit when Bradshaw mentioned in print – for instance – Clark entertaining William Waldegrave. I knew Clark considered William almost as wet as me. William thought Clark bad as well as mad. It was wildly unlikely that they would be hobnobbing together by choice. We tried to get some of this detail right, to meld reality and fantasy. Alan subsequently muttered about breaches of hospitality, since I only knew that he kept a tank in the garden of his house in Sutherland because I had been to dinner there as his guest. I pointed out that I had been discretion itself, in only letting on to Bradshaw about the tank, and not mentioning the astonishing collection of heavy automatic weapons cluttering up the hall and the kitchen.

From the outset, we were delighted to see how much attention the column attracted, some of it from enraged readers who did indeed think the MP for Kensington & Chelsea was writing it himself.

The Bradshaw version had been running in the *Evening Standard* for a month or two when the great diarist himself came on the phone to me. We exchanged pleasantries, and then he got to the point:

'Look, this Diary nonsense has got to stop. My publishers are *really* upset. They say what you are doing will hurt sales of my real *Diaries*, and you know I believe the *Diaries* must be allowed to mature for a few years, like good wine. People are saying they think it's really *me* who's writing in the *Standard*.'

'Come off it, Alan – how could it hurt sales of your *Diaries*? It's a very good joke – people keep telling me it's the best thing in the paper. Our lawyers assure me we're on absolutely safe ground. And anyway, when did you ever mind a bit of publicity?'

'No, this is *serious* – I *mean* it. My lawyers say we have a case against you, and if you won't stop, we shall have to *make* you. I mean, I don't *want* to do this but it *can't* go on'.

'Sorry Al – you've got your lawyers and we've got our lawyers. We don't stop Bradshaw till we are told we have to.'

'Oh. Well, there won't be any *hard feelings*, will there, if I take this up with the lawyers?'

'Not a bit – may the best man win.'

Truth to tell, I thought Alan was having me on. He had already telephoned Peter a couple of times to protest about the pastiche. But how could a man whose whole public life had been an exercise in shameless self-promotion, who fantasised in his own published *Diaries* about jumping on strange girls in railway carriages, possibly mind being teased in the *Evening Standard*?

But he did, he did. Despite our own lawyers' continuing belief that Clark possessed no shred of a case against the *Standard*, as the months went by and the legal process ground on, it became evident that the plaintiff was determined to go to trial to stop Peter Bradshaw. I discussed the case with Associated Newspapers' chairman, Sir David English. We believed we must fight this one, I said, and that whatever the outcome it could do the *Standard* no harm. Our laywers thought we had at least an 80 per cent chance of success. But we had to recognise that, if we lost, there would be a substantial six-figure bill. David and Lord Rothermere are agreeably robust about matters of this kind. Both agreed that we were right to go to court with Clark.

As we advanced towards the trial date in December 1997, Alan and I lunched together at Wiltons, on my invitation. We did not talk much about the case, by mutual tacit consent, but chatted a good deal about the lamentable state of the Tory Party. Alan characteristically dropped a few crumbs that he knew would find their way into Bradshaw: 'To be *absolutely* frank, I'm only going to this *ridiculous* thing of the Leader's at the Savoy because it will give me a line for the Diary.' *His* Diary, he meant, of course

– but it got into Bradshaw first. Alan always talks in italics. The Clark sense of mischief makes indiscretion irresistible – which is one reason I have always gone on liking the old monster, even when others expected me to be enraged by his court action against us.

He had given me fair warning. Now I thought I understood what he was up to. Approaching 70, after a lifetime of naughtiness, he had suddenly decided that he wanted to become an *homme sérieux*. Preposterous as the idea might seem to those who knew him, he fancied recognition as an elder statesman – hence the bizarre television *History of the Conservative Party* which he was even then writing and presenting. To be mocked by Peter Bradshaw in the *Evening Standard*, to see himself weekly portrayed as an ageing right-wing *roué*, jarred intolerably with Alan's new self-image. His sense of comedy, of the grotesque and ridiculous, did not extend to himself.

Perhaps he did not even perceive that his own *Diaries*, peerless insight though they offer into the political life, exposed their author as surely as any parody. Even the greatest diarists tend to diminish their personal reputations by self-revelation, however greatly they enhance their literary standing. So it was for Alan. He achieved fame, but also invited ridicule. His delusions were of a kind from which many of us suffer, but which few reveal. Peter Bradshaw merely played with piercing skill upon the absurdities Clark exposed in his own *Diaries*. Clark claimed to believe that the Bradshaw parody was stealing the bread from his own mouth, was making money for the *Evening Standard* out of exploiting an image Alan was determined to maintain as his own commercial monopoly.

Yet his ambivalence about the struggle persisted, right up to the courtroom door. Early in the autumn, I received a charming postcard from his Scottish eyrie: 'How's our case going? You are a total wanker – presumably on hols, yrs Alan'. Friend or foe? Yet our lawyers reported that the Clark team had been trawling London to gather evidence of folk great and small who professed themselves misled by our Diary, and had collected an impressive body of the deluded, from the porter at Albany to former Defence Secretary Tom King. Yes, he was determined to go the distance.

So we went to court, and as all the world knows, after days of hilarious evidence, we lost. Or rather, the judge found the *Evening Standard* guilty of 'passing off'. But he also accepted our right to continue to publish Peter Bradshaw's parody, provided that the heading was changed to make it even more transparently clear that Bradshaw, and not Clark, was the author of our Diary. After Alan's cross-examination, he and I found ourselves leaving court together. He turned to me in the corridor and remarked savagely, 'Your man made a pretty fair cock-up of that, didn't he?'

Well, yes and no. The outcome of the case was a curious and pyrrhic vistory for the plaintiff. The parody which had upset him was to continue, having generated publicity for the *Evening Standard* of a kind millions could not buy, in every newspaper in the land. Peter found himself famous. Even many of Alan's personal friends were baffled and a little saddened, that this would-be laughing cavalier had brought down the full might of the law, backed by his own millions, upon a humble newspaper columnist's tease.

Nobody in his right mind likes going to court, and nobody likes to lose a legal action. But not a man in our camp, from Lord Rothermere downwards, regretted the decision to fight Alan all the way. The Clark legal assault resembled, in Saki's phrase, the spectacle of a cow trying to tease a gadfly. I would not seek to make too much of any great issues of press freedom here, but we sincerely believed that it was necessary to defend our right to satirize a politician, especially one with such a mania for self-publicity on his own terms. No public figure should expect to write his own school reports. I was asked afterwards if I felt any illwill towards Alan Clark. I answered that I had promised Alan from the outset that there would be no hard feelings. There were indeed none on our side, save towards the judge and our own counsel, who we felt had made a pretty heavy-handed fist of the case. But we chose our lawyers and we paid them, so that was our own lookout. I shall always believe that the verdict was wrong, because the standards of disclaimer which the judge sought to require from the newspaper, to make plain Peter Bradshaw's authorship of our 'Clark Diary', seemed absurdly stringent. The judge reached his decision upon the basis that readers who glanced casually at the *Evening Standard* had been and could continue to be misled into supposing that Alan himself was the author of Bradshaw's pastiche. Yet there will always be readers of anything who get the wrong end of the stick if they do not look at the directions properly. We had carried the Bradshaw byline prominently at the head of each column, yet we were told that this was not enough. By the judge's line of reasoning, a motorist who is incinerated after an explosion caused by dropping a lighted cigarette at a petrol station could have a case against the petrol station for not carrying big enough NO SMOKING signs.

Never mind. Our hugely entertaining day – or rather, week – in court came to an end. The Diary sailed triumphantly on with a bigger audience than ever, until in April 1998 we decided that it had run its natural course for the time being. It will reappear on occasions when we feel that the Great Diarist's views on great events will add to the gaiety of the nation – or, at least, of *Evening Standard* readers. Alan and I got back more or less on speaking terms. He sent me his Christmas card of himself and Jane atop a Scottish mountain, with a scrawled 'thanks for all your help getting me the Kensington & Chelsea seat', but I fear didn't make his usual appearance at my Christmas party. I doubt whether I shall get him to pay for my lunch for a while. Peter Bradshaw has moved on to parodies new, getting better all the time.

Many of our readers, as well as Peter's colleagues, cherish the memory of 'Alan Clark's Diary' in the *Evening Standard* as a small work of art which brought laughter into all our lives, and week after week for a year maintained the highest tradition of literary parody. Bradshaw is glad he wrote it. I'm tremendously pleased that we published it; so too is an army of expensive lawyers. As for the old monster himself, Alan must face the fact that 'Not the Alan Clark Diary' has become part of his personal legend for better or worse – twice as famous because he tried to kick against the pricks. Had he been a trifle more economical with the *légalité*, Peter's barbs might have less injured his marvellous conceit in the end.

Max Hastings
June 1998

1997

Chronology

Selected as candidate for K&C   21 January
Off to fight the Election   24 March
A chat with Paddy Mayhew   26 March
Dreams about the Lady   27 March
MORI poll boosts NAC   4 April
Martin Bell stands against Neil Hamilton
    in Tatton   7 April
Discovers Bradshaw's spoof column   10 April
Judge Harkess returns to haunt NAC   15 April
A swim in the Serpentine   22 April
Poll sees Conservatives catching up   23 April
Invited on to GMTV; a visit to
    Michael Winner   26 April
Edwina Currie criticises Conservatives   27 April
Visits Princess Diana at Kensington Palace   30 April
Tony Blair wins General Election; NAC
    wins K&C for Conservatives   2 May
Tory leadership contest begins   6 May
Encounters Claire Ward MP in the
    Commons   7 May
Ann Widdecombe says Michael Howard
    has 'something of the night'   12 May
Prepares for Victory Party in the
    Commons   13 May
Initiates lawsuit against Bradshaw and the
    Evening Standard   20 May
Fails to get Vice-Chairmanship of the
    1922 Committee   21 May
House-buying   27 May
Mass at Westminster Cathedral   29 May
Recommends knighthood for Max

Hastings	6 June
Tory leadership campaign parties	9 June
Jonathan Aitken comes to stay	21 June
Adventures in Kinlochbervie	22 June
Sir David Frost's party	25 June
Handover of Hong Kong	29 June
Gordon Brown's emergency Budget	2 July
William Hague addresses Tory luncheon	9 July
Countryside Rally	11 July
Murder of Gianni Versace	15 July
Death of Sir James Goldsmith	20 July
Government sop for Paddy Ashdown	24 July
Letter from the Leader	27 July
BBC cameraman sues for being bitten by one of NAC's dogs	9 August
A visit from Nick Soames	17 August
The Notting Hill Carnival	25 August
Death of Princess Diana	31 August
The funeral	7 September
NAC's television *History of the Tory Party* begins	14 September
Hears of brother Colin's autobiography	16 September
Lunch with Jonathan Aitken	23 September
Conservative Party Conference in Blackpool	6 October
How to solve the Irish Question	7 October
Piers Merchant stands down	14 October
Sympathises with Lorna Fitzsimmons	19 October
Conservative bonding weekend	21 October
A phone call from Gerry Adams	25 October
NAC wins court case over his dogs	31 October
Memories of Bernie Ecclestone	12 November
The Michael Hutchence tragedy	23 November

The political assassination of
    Humphrey   24 November
Geoffrey Robinson in trouble   2 December
Court action against Bradshaw and
    the *Evening Standard* begins   15 December
A brilliant performance in the
    witness box   16 December

Eriboll   *Monday, 20 January 1997*

Christ.

Only five days to go before the Day of Judgment: the day when Kensington and Chelsea decides whether or not it wants Clark to represent it in the House of Commons. I was rather short with Jane this morning at breakfast about how she should dress for the interview, and since then there has been something of a *froideur*.

Things have been a little bit tense. Do I really want to go back in the Commons anyway? No one with any class, bloody little Mandelson and Blair in charge of the shop.

On the other hand, it could be rather fun, like being under the Lady after '75.

Took the SS 100 up to 87 mph in the afternoon and took a call on the mobile from a little man who said he's chairman of the Kensington and Chelsea party, asking about my approach to constituency surgeries.

Why can't these people mind their own *business*?

Albany   *Tuesday, 21 January*

I have coasted through to the last six, in the process seeing off a platoon of oiks – including Winston Churchill MP, grandson of the great man and a walking, talking disproof of any talent-and-heredity theory that might still be knocking about.

I am now up against a jowly lawyer and keen basher of the Kraut-loving Brussels bureaucrats: one Martin Howe. He has the same scintillating conversational skill of his treacherous uncle Geoffrey – i.e., don't drive or operate

heavy machinery afterwards. I look forward to breaking the
captain's bats over his fat little head.

The other finalists include Hugo Summerson[1], a ghastly
little smoothie who looks like a Swiss ski-lift operator we
once saw in Zermatt. On the distaff side, there's a banker
called Sarah Whitehouse – lovely short hair. A definite
frisson. Mmmm.

To celebrate, I took the SS 100 up to 97 mph in
Kensington High Street, while indulging in a reverie of
little Rifkind walking across an Angolan minefield. And
then! Invited into Cabinet! The Foreign Office! And, after
that, who knows . . . ?

The WPc was very charming, with a lovely trim little
uniform.

Albany   *Wednesday, 22 January*

Final selection tomorrow. Not much to do but wait.
Boisterous lunch with Bruce[2] at the Connaught, during
which he seemed to get through most of a herd. We
managed a Palmer, a Pichon Longueville and some
Montrachet and some *digestifs*. Afterwards, we agreed that
Kensington and Chelsea was going to be a pushover.

As when the Führer looked at the pathetic decadent
Soviet empire, it's only going to take one good *kick* for the
whole rotten edifice to come crashing down before me.
And then my tanks will be rolling down the Brompton

---

[1] Conservative MP for Walthamstow 1987–92.
[2] Bruce Anderson, political editor of the *Spectator* and close friend of
  Not Alan Clark (hereafter NAC).

Road! Took the SS 100 up to 107 mph in Pall Mall with Bruce in the passenger seat singing 'Tomorrow Belongs to Me'.

Kensington Town Hall, midnight   *Thursday, 23 January*

Victory!

I have been taking congratulations all evening! Happy days are here again! Suddenly Jane came through the crush of admirers, holding my mobile gingerly. 'It's Margaret,' she hissed. I snapped to attention, but the signal was faint. 'Alan . . .' she quavered, 'you must carry on the flame . . .'

And then the line went dead.

Albany   *Monday, 24 March*

Well, the Election campaign has begun in earnest.

Tricky night at Lyall Street with Jimmy [Goldsmith] and Aspers.[1] I am writing this with a tiny cut on the temple, sustained, entirely accidentally, when Jimmy hit me with a backgammon board.

I sensed the Führerbunker atmosphere the moment I stepped through the door. Aspers subdued, Jimmy talking, talking, and pacing rather incessantly. He had a lot of ripped paperwork from MORI spread over a table which

---

[1] John Aspinall, founder of Howlett's Zoo Park and the Claremont Club, and supporter of Sir James Goldsmith's Referendum Party.

had a big map of Britain with flags on and a big stain where Carla Powell[1] managed to spill a tray of vodka martinis the other week.

At one stage, Jimmy actually screamed at the mention of Bob Worcester, whose MORI poll disclosed such unflattering results for the Referendum Party; my eardrums are still ringing.

The tricky moment came when we were playing backgammon, and I had sportingly allowed Jimmy to take £1,200 or so off me – the kind of social work I feel obliged to do since he agreed not to make trouble by getting any of his chinless inverts to stand against me in Kensington and Chelsea.

Then I thoughtlessly but innocently asked him what he'd be up to after 1 May, and will it be a relief not to have anything to do with politics? He bellowed with rage and gesticulated with the board, catching me rather painfully just above the eye.

The big plus was seeing Charlotte Blacker, Jimmy's *very* attractive agent. At 37, the Best Before date is a bit of a distant memory, but even so . . . Very lively, though apparently slightly deaf, so she shouts. Our conversations, therefore, could not be discreet. A definite charge, however . . .

Albany   *Wednesday, 26 March*

A little liverish at the moment, I fear, after a little party held

---

[1] Wife of Sir Charles Powell, former foreign-affairs adviser to Margaret Thatcher.

by Paddy Mayhew[1] to celebrate his imminent release from the Northern Ireland Office. I turned up expecting to find Paddy pretty well demob happy. Actually he was very low, having rather enjoyed himself at the NIO, God help him. He was especially down about his disgraced former subordinate Tim Smith,[2] who is standing down as the Conservative candidate for Beaconsfield, quite broken by this al-Fayed cash-for-questions business.

Soon the place was absolutely heaving with Ministry bureaucrats – the contingent of scruffy Fenians being, as ever, in the substantial majority. All pretty brazen about this enormous tunnel that Sinn Fein/IRA managed to build to get them out of the Maze.

Individual H-blocks are now like self-governing trusts, I told Paddy genially. 'They've opted out of local authority control and now they're grant-maintained, able to spend their budget of UK taxpayers' money on huge murals of Good King Billy, Bobby Sands, or what have you, without interference from the warders.'

Poor Paddy was not cheered up by my badinage. Not surprising. The whole thing close to the Great Maze Escape of '83 and all the egg on the face of poor old Nick Scott when he was Min of State – and my predecessor at Kensington and Chelsea. A bad omen.

---

[1] Lord (Patrick) Mayhew of Twysden, Conservative MP for Royal Tunbridge Wells 1974–83; Tunbridge Wells 1983–97; former Northern Ireland Secretary.
[2] Conservative MP for Beaconsfield 1982–97.

Albany   *Thursday, 27 March*

The Tim Smith business has really hit us hard. At least he got it out of the way before the Easter weekend, but even so. I telephoned Herr Doktor Mawhinney,[1] asking if we might actually find a berth for Nick Scott at Beaconsfield, and got some ripe Ulster abuse for my pains.

Needless to say, Labour Nouveau types have been giddily parading for the cameras this morning with silly suppressed grins as if it's Eights Week at Oxford or the lull before VE Day.

I want to slap their bespectacled, pink little faces when they smugly talk about not taking anything for granted, but very obviously they think their 150-plus landslide is now in the bag, and soon Major and Heseltine will be broken, humiliated men.

Could I bear it? Could I bear frightful biddies like Tessa Blackstone and Mary Warnock preening themselves at being allowed out of their box for five years?

I woke at 3 this morning after a nightmare. The Lady had accepted a position in Blair's first Cabinet as Heritage Minister i/c Lottery scratchcards. I had to stand by an open window for some minutes to calm down.

Albany   *Friday, 4 April*

I really am doing tremendously well at the moment.

---

[1] Sir Brian Mawhinney, Conservative MP for Cambridgeshire North West since 1997; a Cabinet Minister in the last Government, and organiser of the 1997 Election campaign.

The papers have got some sort of MORI poll about
how awfully the Party is doing in London: yards of silly
statistics compiled by Bob Worcester's clipboard-wonks,
and fed into some contraption that turns them into pie
charts. But it says that I have a 'plus' personality factor – six
points higher than the Conservatives' London-wide
average!

And just to make things even more exquisite, little
Mellor has apparently got a 'minus' personality factor: well
below the average.

I inspected my reflection in the mirror and, yes, I am
looking quite 20 years younger. To celebrate, I took the SS
100 up to 121 mph in Exhibition Road and in a dreamy
reverie I wondered on what pretext I could *discuss* Mellor's
Kiss-of-Death approval rating with him. Perhaps Barbara[1]
could convene some spasmoid 'strategy' meeting with
Mellor purely to allow me to jeer and gloat over how
unpopular he is.

What *fun*.

Later, I breakfasted on a single kipper and went for a
stroll in Kensington Gardens, and some very attractive
Italian girls rollerbladed past me, shouting, 'Meester Clark!
Prime Meeeeneeestaire!'

It is all I deserve.

Albany   *Monday, 7 April*

Christ! I opened *The Times* today to find that Mandelson
and Ashdown have clubbed together to fight off

---

[1] Barbara Lord, NAC's Election agent.

Hamilton[1] in Tatton, and withdrawn their own contenders to give a clear field to Martin Bell, the BBC's Male Menopause Candidate.

Little Bell is deeply smug with a Persil-white suit and that strange I-speak-your-weight-machine voice they all have. Apparently he'd been on more or less continuous gardening leave at the BBC prior to collecting his gold watch, and this is going to be his last hurrah in front of the cameras.

He has a look of an old retainer of Pa's at Saltwood who used to wear a white coat to polish the silver, and was always lecturing below-stairs staff in a strange, halting voice: 'Honesty. Is the best. Policy.' The local police finally found him chinking along the railway-station platform at midnight, his white-jacket pockets bulging with antique cutlery.

However, it does not look as if Hamilton is in any way 'frit', as the Lady would say. Rather, he is being kept up to snuff by his lady wife, Christine, who looks as if she bends iron bars with her teeth and is shaping up to be the Elspeth Howe of her generation.

Albany   *Tuesday, 8 April*

Fool, Clark, fool, fool! I am in the deepest doghouse. The local Chairman will not speak to me. The Party Chairman will not speak to me. Jane will not speak to me.

Today, have made a terrible blunder.

---

[1] Neil Hamilton, Conservative MP for Tatton 1983–97, disgraced over the Mohamed al-Fayed 'cash-for-questions' affair.

I was having a fairly bullish lunch today with Bruce at Wiltons, in the course of which he managed to wipe out the livestock population of Northern Europe. Bruce asked me what position I'd want in Cabinet. Calling for a second bottle of the '61 Palmer, I said I'd settle for Defence, as long as I can revise my 'Options For Change' paper. Then he asked me if I'd be talking about that in my forthcoming defence lecture to the Royal United Services Institute in Whitehall and when was that anyway?

My blood ran cold. I slapped my forehead. 'What time is it?' I gasped. 'Only half-past one,' muttered Bruce, puzzled. 'Oh my God,' I said. 'The ****ing thing's today!' Together Bruce and I ran out and jumped into the SS 100 and roared down Jermyn Street at 170 mph, my lecture notes fluttering out into the slipstream like snowflakes. The engine blew up in St James's.

Then my mobile went, and Bruce with splendid presence of mind answered it. I heard a livid voice at the other end. But Bruce was marvellous.

'I'm sorry, but Mr Clark dictated a letter conveying his apologies fully two weeks ago, and he is now on his way to help a friend with the Election,' he said imperiously, and clicked the phone off.

Bless Bruce! We got the RAC out to deal with the car and walked back to Wiltons to tackle some bread-and-butter pudding.

Albany   *Wednesday, 9 April*

What a pain. A collection of Olympic-standard bores from Charter 88 wrote to me recently, inviting me to participate in some balls-aching 'Democracy Day' debate.

Very clearly, the idea was that I was to stand up and defend the export of electro-shock batons to President Mobutu of Zaire – praising their exquisite Midlands craftsmanship and so forth – while a bevy of bearded students expressed their collective longing for the Soviet Union by flinging rotten eggs at me.

A previous engagement loomed; I flipped idly through my diary and dictated a note to Imogen – whose lipstick, I notice, is of a quite ravishingly roseate hue. It was a fine piece of nonsense saying I couldn't go because there might be a prospective candidates' meeting in the Town Hall that day – these events being naturally of supreme importance to me. Some more raillery with my young colleague followed, together with a 180 mph spin down a sunny Bayswater Road in the SS 100 with Imogen laughing deliciously in the passenger seat.

Later I opened *The Times*, to see a very large picture of a lovely young blonde whose perfect features brought back fleeting memories of an ecstatic encounter in a Sixties Swiss ski chalet. She turns out to be Martin Bell's beautiful daughter Melissa, whom he is presenting as his 'Press Secretary'. This has to be Mandelson's cunning idea: little Bell would not have thought of it in a month of Sundays. I sense that Mrs Christine Hamilton's handsome features are going to be a little discomposed by young Melissa's new prominence. Hee hee.

Afternoon
My good mood has been soured by the fact that I discovered that this Charter 88 beardie collective has scuttled off tearfully to sneak to the K&C Council, who said there were no plans for a cross-party debate that day, and then some outfit called the World Council of

Churches got in on the act, claiming that I had already snubbed precisely this sort of inter-party 'debate', whingeing that I declined to commit myself to attending the ghastly Marxist love-in that *they'd* organised. Imogen is going to claim the hard disk drive on my diary computer is corrupted.

But *bugger* anyway.

Albany   *Thursday, 10 April*

This really is intolerable. Somebody called Bradshaw in the *Evening Standard* is writing a spoof of my *Diaries*. I feel like the Chief Executive of Kentucky Fried Chicken when he walks down the High Street and sees some grime-infested stall called Tennessee Fried Burgers whose patrons are staggering out in the streets, whooping and gibbering with BSE – and swearing henceforth to boycott Kentucky Fried Chicken.

Cheek. I phoned Bruce to ask who this Bradbury was. He had no idea. So I telephoned little Bradford this morning at his office down the road. He sounded surprised; presumably I'd caught him in the midst of finishing off half a bottle of gin and fiddling his expenses. I gave him the gentlest and most lenient of wiggings, explaining that people are getting the wrong impression from this sort of nonsense, and that these three-shilling notes he is peddling in the streets are undermining the currency. I hope that this is an end to the matter.

My mood was lightened later in the evening by my triumphant performance at the Constituency adoption meeting – I secured a unanimous vote, having effortlessly

located the G-spot of thousands of cheering Kensington
ladies flinging their under-garments at me.

Saltwood   *Monday, 14 April*

A little dyspeptic after last night's birthday dinner.

Bruce was placed next to Robert,[1] and opposite
Norman.[2] The wines were various and the conversation
lively, as ever, especially when it turned to whether we
should abolish the pound sterling in favour of the
Reichsmark that Kohl and his sundry Vichy satellites are
keen on.

Norman turned to me crossly for support but I'm afraid
I was in full official-candidate mode: options open, wait
and see, that sort of thing. Butter would not melt.

I had a strange dream last night that someone had told
me that 'Judge' Harkess,[3] that sinister paterfamilias and
wearer of the cuckold's horns, had returned to London to
torment me. Absurd, of course, yet disturbingly vivid and
realistic.

At dawn this morning, I drove up to London in the
Porsche. I do not feel 69, nothing like it. In fact, the closer
I get to returning to the House, the centre of political

---

[1] Viscount Cranborne, Leader of the Opposition in the Lords since
    1997 and a good friend of NAC.
[2] Lord (Norman) Tebbit of Chingford, Conservative MP for Epping
    1970–74; Chingford 1974–92.
[3] James Harkess, a retired judge, had threatened to horsewhip Clark
    when he discovered that Clark had seduced his wife and two
    daughters.

power, the younger I feel, like Siegfried approaching Fafner's cave ecstatically to grasp the mystical treasure: the helmet and the Ring!

I feel power and victory surging gloriously through my body. I am invincible!

Albany   *Tuesday, 15 April*

Oh my God, it was not a dream. Harkess really is back, here to excoriate my 'dishonesty' and campaign for New Labour, if you please.

It is like those awful horror films where you think the monster is finally dead and then it rears up right at the end for one last terrible screech before the credits. I am a little rattled. It is not, to use the spasmoid Smith Square terminology, 'helpful'.

I have had the Constituency Chairman on the phone for what seemed like three hours, exhaustively going over the 'line to take'. There was a distinct tone of rebuke.

Damn. After all our hard work on the stump, trying to draw a veil over it all. Jane has been so wonderful with the constituents, shaking everyone's hand, talking about their flowers, their gardens, their dogs. Now this.

Oh, Clark, why, why, in the name of God, why? Why that insane indiscretion with Valerie and her lovely daughters, Joie and Ali?

Were they in London as well? I suddenly wondered. Perhaps I could arrange a discreet supper with them at the Ritz – wasn't that where Joie liked? – while the Judge was out howling his denunciations of me to Radio Gosforth, or whoever it was.

Dangerously excited, I found my old number for them, and dialled. But all I got was an elderly Cypriot who spoke no English. Blast.

Albany   *Wednesday, 16 April*

Well really. Harkess is thoroughly chippy and absurd. He has now given some preposterous interview saying, 'The sacrament of marriage is very important,' and. 'That someone like that could get such a plum seat makes my blood boil,' but that he had forgiven me.

I kept my temper and told the television interviewer, 'Well, that's very generous of him and very Christian of him.'

This whole grotesque charade seems to be a stunt to promote some absurd book he's written. What next? Will he pose for the tabloids again, brandishing some silly little whip in return for some heartbreakingly small sum of money? I would not be surprised if little Max Clifford was waiting in the wings, ready to present Harkess with a large bill.

I shall now rewrite the manifesto, claiming that, if elected, I will string Harkess up by his thumbs outside Gloucester Road Underground station and from dawn till dusk on 2 May, every passer-by may slap him. A landslide beckons.

Albany   *Tuesday, 22 April*

I have been swimming this morning at dawn in the Serpentine. The police fenced off the area for me, and it was thrillingly cold and clear as I cut through the water with my powerful crawl, like Byron crossing the Hellespont, the sky a pale blue, the traffic from Kensington Gore a distant, bee-like murmur.

I have never felt so tinglingly alive, so intoxicatingly on the verge of political power. My muscle tone has *definitely* improved. However, as I was doing my vigorous butterfly towards the bank, with Barbara in the car with the leaflets, and Jane ready by the bank with my extra-large true-blue towel, I heard a Danish backpacking tourist say, 'Is that old man drowning?' Flipping over to backstroke, I was about to shout a riposte, but unfortunately managed to swallow about a pint and a half of water and two officers had to wade in to get me out. Rather ignominious.

Little Santer[1] has done us a tremendous good turn. The contest has become who can be the most beastly to the Germans and that is a game our side will always win. I even took a call from Jimmy on my mobile in the back of the car, raving about it being 'one minute to midnight'. But it was difficult to make out exactly what he was saying, over the sound of his helicopter.

I see little Blair's father-in-law has given the cry of '*A la lanterne*' for all *Telegraph* readers. Apparently he was in *Dad's Army* or something, presumably playing one of the chaps in the second or third row who never got to say anything.

---

[1] Jacques Santer, President of the European Commission, had called Eurosceptics 'doom-mongers'.

Amused to note that Meyer,[1] the elderly baronet who attempted to plunge his rubber dagger between the Lady's shoulder-blades, looks like withholding his support from me. A profound relief. The man is like some forgotten member of the Addams family, although his cadaverous appearance did not hinder his success with women, I pondered, inspecting the fold of skin on my neck in the wing-mirror.

Jane and I took to the stump with a spring in our step, and short of actually having the Spice Girls in the car with us, the response from the people could not be more ecstatic. I am mobbed everywhere I go. I am thinking of touring the streets on horseback.

Albany   *Wednesday, 23 April*

I am almost delirious with excitement. The opinion polls have got little Blair falling back badly, and our side catching up on the inside rail.

Down to five points! The way things are going, we'll be a nose ahead by tomorrow week – a majority of ten to fifteen seats! Bruce proved it by doing a little graph for me on the back of the menu at Wilton's over lunch.

Can it be true? I thought this victory stuff was just Heseltine putting a brave face on it all, doing his old-trouper act for the last time. But no. This could be our El Alamein, the turning point. In *government* again. And then

---

[1] Sir Anthony Meyer, Conservative MP for Eton and Slough 1964–6; Flint West 1970–83; Clwyd North West 1983–92. Initiated a 'stalking horse' leadership bid against Margaret Thatcher in 1989.

. . . who knows? Will the PM give me a job? Something in Cabinet? I would settle for Trade, even the NIO. Trembling with emotion, I called Alastair's[1] office and asked to speak to him. But once I gave my name, his secretary gave me some spasmoid line about him being 'in a meeting'.

Hmmm. It could be that I will never get anything from little Major. What should we do after 2 May? It might have to be the Stauffenberg option. Perhaps I shall convene some little 'dinner party' at Saltwood with Howard, Portillo, Lilley, apple-cheeked young Hague – all decent Wehrmacht officers, thinking of what is best for the Party and best for the Fatherland. We will arrive at Chequers with our explosives metaphorically primed.

However, if things go wrong, little Major and his Eurobores have a large coil of piano wire ready and waiting . . .

Saltwood   *Saturday, 26 April*

These are dark days. Our glorious fightback in the polls has disappeared, just when we were surging up the field. It is just like when that bald motor-racing commentator shouts that Damon Hill *must* win – invariably the cue for all four of his tyres to explode.

The papers are talking about a landslide, the biggest since Attlee. All balls, of course, and yet worrying. I telephoned Mawhinney to get some sense of what was

---

[1] Alastair Goodlad, Conservative MP for Eddisbury since 1983 and Chief Whip in the last Government.

happening in the Bunker, but one of his tearful little teenage staff wouldn't put me through — while in the background I could hear what sounded like a speeded-up 78 rpm recording of the Reverend Ian Paisley.

Smith Square is not a happy ship, and little Mawhinney seems to have lost control, quarrelling with Saatchi, shouting at everyone. He is like a labrador we once had at Eriboll — loyal but headstrong; finally it 'turned' and started attacking local children. I am afraid that, once 2 May arrives, Mawhinney will be led out to the vet's van, where a large hypodermic awaits.

This week has been a little trying.

On Thursday night some idiot from GMTV rang me up, asking if I would come into the studio and enlarge on my comments in this column. I was crisp with him and replaced the receiver. When I finally got back to sleep, I had a nightmare that the Lady was doing aerobics on GMTV, wearing a blue leotard.

The only rather tricky moment for Jane and me last week was having to visit the palatial Kensington mansion of Michael Winner. He would keep addressing me as 'Al', repeating the parts in my manifesto about bringing back the rope, and positively glowed when I pointed out the postcard of Hitler on his mantelpiece.

He asked me what I thought of the décor; I congratulated him on being 'unencumbered with any debilitating preoccupation with "taste"'.

He seemed delighted with that, and insisted on getting us to pose with him for a photograph and, as a fellow *News of the World* columnist, I could hardly refuse.

Saltwood   *Sunday, 27 April*

Today the papers are even worse, and Mrs Currie has dumped all over us. Yet I feel euphoria flooding through me. All the signs are that after the Big Push on Thursday, Waldegrave, Rifkind, Lang and Forsyth will all have bought it, possibly Shephard and Newton too.[1] The Party will be like England after the Great War, when the ladies of England's great families could scarcely remember which of their menfolk were dead and which alive.

Yet it leaves the field clear for me! I will surely be invited to join the shadow Cabinet, and then the Party will need an elder statesman to lead it out of the wilderness. I shall be 74 in 2002, but what of that? Winston was 77 when he came back in '51.

Intoxicated with the thrill of imminent power, I bounded up to the top of the towers, where I hung on the bar and effortlessly did 30 pull-ups, and then swung round 360 degrees, over and over again.

Carried away as I spun, I yelled, *'Ich bin der Übermensch!'* at which point the bar gave way and I collapsed into a pile of masonry, and Jane and the staff had to dig me out, rather gallingly.

---

[1] William Waldegrave, Conservative MP for Bristol West 1979–97; Sir Malcolm Rifkind, Conservative MP for Edinburgh Pentlands 1974–97; Lord (Ian) Lang, Conservative MP for Galloway 1979–83, Galloway and Upper Nithsdale 1983–97; Sir Michael Forsyth, Conservative MP for Stirling 1983–97; Gillian Shephard, Conservative MP for Norfolk South West since 1987; Tony Newton, Conservative MP for Braintree 1974–97. All former Cabinet Ministers

Albany   *Monday, 28 April*

I took the Porsche up from Kent to London – 22 minutes, best time ever.

An intriguing situation has developed here in the Constituency. The Royal Borough of Kensington and Chelsea's latest newsletter contains not one picture of me in 24 pages, and quite a number of our beloved Council leader, one Joan Hanham – a would-be contender for the parliamentary seat, who did not even make the shortlist of six.

I am mentally savouring possible responses to this . . . shall I call it a slight? But however I respond, it will make my impending victory all the sweeter.

Helicopter, en route, 3 p.m.   *Wednesday, 30 April*

I am writing this squashed up in a helicopter that the local Party has hired for the frantic last days of the General Election campaign. It is *vital* that we are able to get from one end of the Constituency to the other in a matter of seconds.

It is wonderful to sweep through the blazing blue empyrean and see my new territories spread below me: Kensington Gardens, Holland Park, the Victoria and Albert Museum like a red-brick russet jewel in its verdant setting. I can hardly breathe with excitement.

Jane looks a little pale. Perhaps taking her up in the 'copter after Wiltons was a mistake, but she *needed* a good lunch before campaigning; it would have been a shame for her to miss out on the angels-on-horseback. I do wish Bruce would move up and give us both a bit of room. He could at least stay awake.

3.17 p.m.
My God. We have just swept low over Kensington Palace and *she* was there, outside, sunbathing in a ravishing black one-piece swimsuit.

She is a goddess. She is Diana, and I am Actaeon! I am certain that she smiled up at me. I am taking command of the controls. We shall land in her private grounds and I will canvass my future constituent personally.

5.30 p.m.
Most satisfactory.

I made a perfect landing just by Her sunbed; switched off the engines and wondered briefly why I could still hear that thunderous drone. (Bruce snoring.) I ripped off the headphones and advanced boldly, while Jane and the others remained in the helicopter.

She pushed her sunglasses up on to her forehead and greeted me in that adorably C2 accent that always makes me go weak at the knees. I wondered if I might discuss the dangers of a federal Europe with her. She motioned me into her private apartments, and we were away for half an hour. I returned in high good humour and informed everyone, '*There's* someone whose support we can rely on.'

Jane got into a bit of a bate and it was 'no speaks' for the rest of the afternoon.

Albany, 10 p.m.   *Thursday, 1 May*

This is it. Zero hour has finally arrived. Jane and I have

repaired briefly here to rest and recover after the last day on the stump: spent largely touring around Safeway on Kensington High Street, and graciously accepting the unalloyed adoration, if not hysteria, of the well-heeled, middle-aged electorate.

I am going to change, have a quick drink, and Jane is going to put her face on again and transform herself with a beautiful black evening dress I picked out personally for her last night.

On the television, both the little Dimblebys are talking about a landslide according to their wretched exit polls. All their female 'reporters' out in the constituencies – quite indistinguishable, it seems to me, from all New Labour's cloned, power-suited women candidates – are gloating. I turn the set off.

Kensington Town Hall, 12.10 a.m.   *Friday, 2 May*

We have arrived in the Town Hall: that strange redbrick complex oddly and unpleasantly reminiscent of the new British Library monstrosity. I am now writing this in a little ante-chamber off the entrance lobby.

When Jane and I walked in with the Mayor, there was a shower of journalists and other undesirables crowded around a television set in the downstairs annexe, insolently cheering every Labour gain.

I walked up to a group of them and found myself face to face with little Bradshaw, who has had the temerity to write a travesty of my *Diaries* in the *Evening Standard*. He quailed in my presence, as well he might. I was civil enough but my manner clearly conveyed with what saintly restraint I forbore to give him the hiding he so richly deserved.

4 a.m.
Well, little Blair and his spin doctors are the masters now. I had 19,887 to the Labour man's 10,000 odd. Majority a bit dented, our side staying grumpily at home, some bad feeling over Nick Scott. Still, I am the last bastion of the true blue Tory Empire! And to be back in the House, the sweetness of victory, sweet, sweet, intensified by seeing the expressions on the faces of those Eurobores and unreliables given the bum's rush.

We were able to watch it all on a little portable television in a room off the main hall. Waldegrave, Mellor, Lang, Rifkind – all out! Each time we sang out, 'Tory gain! Tory gain!' and Jane and I did a little jig. The expression on Mellor's face alone was worth the price of admission.

My acceptance speech was in the traditional vein, starting with a ringing vote of thanks for the 'police': always a nice touch, I think, implying that my opponents are crooks, who have been thwarted in an essentially criminal act. Then an elegant gesture towards the Returning Officer, and I indulged in some self-congratulation about how much better I'd done than the Party nationally. No nonsense about congratulating the other chap on a fair fight.

I *did* enjoy myself. There were some very jolly young people dressed up as the Teddy Bear Party, including a very sexy blonde girl, and I particularly liked the look of Miss Angela Ellis-Jones of the UK Independence Party (540 votes – not bad!), a handsome woman who is apparently always in the *Daily Mail* because she has not yet 'known' a man. She rather harshly described me as a 'serial adulterer' but perhaps I might be able to discuss our policy overlap later.

Bad news about Portillo. It looks as if Heseltine may indeed be able to foresee the circumstances in which he will run for the leadership, and is even now getting ready to replay the 1990 contest, only this time ending with his thinning pompadour whisking into Number 10.

Who can stop him? Someone with three ministerial jobs under his belt, someone who is about to publish a history of the Conservative Party, someone who believes in fighting Brussels and its collaborators on the beaches. The battle for 2002 starts now. *Der Sieg wird unser sein . . .*

Albany   *Tuesday, 6 May*

Well, the Tory political landscape is a smoking ruin.

But as the dawn comes up, and Blair's Messerschmidts drone away over the horizon, I am delighted to report that the smart shops and elegant terraces of Kensington and Chelsea are unscathed. The only vote I seem to have lost is that of the film director Michael Winner, who cut up rather rough over my comments about his house in this Diary.[1]

We are in a mess, though, and every revolting little BBC functionary and *Guardian* scribbler with a colleague or homosexual 'partner' on the New Labour benches is gloating.

Little Major has mumbled something about the show

---

[1] Michael Winner, a lifelong Conservative, was so infuriated by NAC's comments about his décor that he voted Labour in the General Election.

being over and it being time to leave the stage. This apparently was a phrase he learned at his father's knee as the old boy, wearing smeared make-up and floppy-toed clown shoes, hid in his dressing room with the lights off while the angry audience demanded their money back.

We have now started a spastic 'leadership contest', which has about as much political significance as the election of a refreshments secretary in a suburban golf club. Heseltine is *hors de combat* with a return of his heart condition, and while he was delirious with pain-killers on his hospital bed, his lady wife, Anne, typed out his withdrawal statement, then gripped his writing hand and wrote out his signature underneath. I'm not sure how he took the news of his standing down. Clarke is standing for the collaboration with Kohl faction, Michael Howard is running on his iron-fist-in-the-iron-glove ticket, apparently with fresh-faced, apple-cheeked young Hague as his supporter, an arrangement toasted over champagne earlier this evening.

No one seems to be begging me to stand.

Albany, morning   *Wednesday, 7 May*

Hague has dumped.

His claque of admirers encouraged him to think of himself as the Young Pretender, and he believes this publicity whole-heartedly. So the engagement is broken off. Now Dorrell is courting the bore vote and Redwood's candidacy is gravely damaged by the support of *The Times*.

A complete shower. I am going to the Commons.

House of Commons, evening

Extraordinary. In the Commons I saw what appeared to be
a crocodile of schoolchildren in the Central Lobby, moving
unimpeded into the Chamber. When I complained,
someone explained that this was the New Labour intake, all
polytechnic lecturers, media folk and Trade Union press
officers, with their electronic pagers dutifully turned off,
and the person at their head barking instructions was little
Mandelson – although what he knows about Parliament
could be written on the back of a stamp.

It is marvellous to be back in the House; I simply can't
believe it has been five years, although it was very strange
to see the sides reversed. I couldn't get used to the through-
the-looking-glass effect – I felt dizzy and disorientated and
had a slight nose-bleed.

We were in Opposition when I first arrived in '74,
when Ted Heath was Leader and it was a disagreeable
shock to see that he is still here, Sir Edward Heath, Father
of the House, still pompous and slow-witted – visibly
bridling when Gwyneth Dunwoody,[1] in her speech proposing dear Betty Boothroyd as Speaker, called him 'Mr'
Heath.

Later I was strolling towards the Strangers' Bar,
whistling a lively air, when I came across a *very* pretty girl
in tears. 'What's the matter?' I asked. The dear little thing
gulped and pouted and said: 'It's my first day. I'm lost . . .'
I twinkled, like Alec d'Urberville. 'Never mind,' I said,
proffering a hanky. 'It's easy for a secretary to get lost on
her first day.' She turned on me, her beautiful eyes flashing
angrily. 'I am Claire Ward, the New Labour Member for
Watford!' she shouted, and ran off down the corridor.

---

[1] Labour MP for Crewe 1973–83; Crewe and Nantwich since 1983.

But she still has my handkerchief – an excuse to get back in touch! How have I existed out of this place?

Albany   *Monday, 12 May*

That's torn it. As I feared, the Party has signally failed to show the spirit of Rorke's Drift. Deeply unnerved by the chanting of New Labour's Zulu warriors, and the hypnotic thrum of their drums, our chaps have started bayoneting each other.

The snaggle-toothed former Prisons Minister Ann Widdecombe[1] has caused much ooo-er. Previously an enthusiast for nothing more than leg-irons on pregnant women prisoners and mini-shackles for their tiny criminal offspring, she has held up a crucifix in front of Michael Howard with a great cry of 'Get thee behind me!'

There is 'something of the night' about him, she says. Pretty rich coming from a woman who has had the neck-bolts airbrushed out of her Election leaflet photo.

Miss Widdecombe is rather excitably *of the faith*, of course, having taken instruction from dear Father Michael Seed. Howard hails from the Estonian wing of the Cabinet, on the other hand. It is this, I fear, which accounts for the culture clash between these two giants of the modern Conservative Party.

I telephoned my old friend Jonathan[2] for news from the

---

[1] Conservative MP for Maidstone 1987–97; Maidstone and the Weald from 1997.

[2] Jonathan Aitken, Conservative MP for Thanet East, 1974–83; Thanet South 1983–97. A former Cabinet Minister.

Howard camp. He said they were poised to hit back jolly hard, chortling that their crack squad of dirty tricks operatives were even now on the phone to the *Daily Mail*. *Vive la guerre!*

Albany   *Tuesday, 13 May*

I'm afraid Jonathan has gone too far. The papers are today full of a lot of transparent balls about Ann Widdecombe's credibility being shot on account of having been seduced by the wiles of the prisons chief, Derek Lewis, that silver-haired, silver-tongued charmer. It was Derek sending Ann chocolates and flowers, Derek and Ann running towards each other in slow motion in a summer meadow, Derek climbing up to Ann's moonlit balcony with a single rose clamped in his teeth.

I am frankly much more excited about my triumphal Victory Party tonight at the Commons. What an exquisite pleasure it promises to be. I had Smythson's print all the invitations before the Election but kept them discreetly in the desk drawer until my vote had been weighed. I couldn't resist invites to the likes of Malcolm Rifkind, Ian Lang and Michael Forsyth! How delicious it will be to welcome them proprietorially to the Commons, and then put on my concerned face: 'How are you? Picked up anything in the way of directorships? Oh dear.'

What *fun*.

Albany   *Wednesday, 14 May*

Last night was a triumph.

The sun was out and the Terrace was glorious. None of the Defeated turned up for me to torture, sadly, and little Major did not show, but it was a delight to see Alastair [Goodlad]. (He once wrote a rather childish pastiche of my *Diaries* suggesting I liked to importune girls outside St James's.) I could even tolerate Lord Archer, whose spivvy little face was inflated into its most absurdly *statesmanlike* expression.

Naturally, my cheerleaders from the Press wished to know who I supported for the leadership. I opined that all the contenders are a motley collection of wankers. Hague is especially unacceptable, as he will be almost entirely bald by the end of this Parliament, although the same could be said about Margaret Beckett. However, he has the support of the Party's homosexual lobby, despite having contrived to get *engaged* – his one politically startling achievement.

But honestly, what a *shower* the Party is now. They don't realise they have to be guerrilla fighters; like the Yugoslav Partisans, hiding out in the forests and mountains. So when little Mandelson and Blair sweep through the village, lounging in the back of their staff car, their jackboots and monocles gleaming in the sun, some sturdy fighter must rush out from the nearest café and lob a stick of dynamite at them – and never mind if the entire village is hanged the next morning in reprisal. They have to blow up bridges, and this lot couldn't blow up a balloon.

Later this afternoon, despite a stinking hangover, I *sparkled* in the House, demanding an end to little Blair's edict abolishing Prime Minister's Questions. I really was on tremendous form; and I even caught the eye of dear Claire, the young New Labour Member for Watford. Her rosebud lips pursed adorably and I'm certain I received the ghost of a coquettish smile! Steady, Clark . . . !

Albany   *Sunday, 18 May*

This means war.

Time and time again I have telephoned young Bradshaw at the *Standard*, and civilly asked him to oblige me with an undertaking not to write any more silly spoofs of my *Diaries*. No such undertaking has been received. So I have decided to bring the full majesty of the law down on his cringing, little head. That will teach him to snigger to me about 'post-modernism'. Impertinence. We shall see how post-modern he looks in the *dock*.

My blood is up. I took the SS 100 from Kent up to town today in 14 minutes, but there was a tremendous jam in the Fulham Road. I was stuck behind some sort of open-topped bus, and I was delighted to see my constituents seemed to be having some sort of delayed street party to celebrate my re-entry into the Commons: true-blue Tory flags and shirts everywhere and everyone cheering wildly as I drove along. Those deracinated oiks at Plymouth never laid on a spread like this. Choking back the tears, I tried standing up and giving an impromptu speech, but I was drowned out by the chanting of names unfamiliar to me. This Rude Gullet (Rod Gillet?) really is popular. Somebody in the Constituency Association? Perhaps if we got him a safe seat *he* could be Chairman of the '22.

Albany   *Monday, 19 May*

I see little Mandelson has attempted to tug at our heartstrings by giving some sort of personal television interview – à la Diana – in which his eyes brimmed with tears. A wasted effort, of course. Most of his New Labour followers will, like me, have assumed that some half-chewed piece of baby had gone down the wrong way.

Today Jane and I popped into the Chelsea Flower Show, and lingered in the Royal Horticultural Society tent for lunch. Ghastly suburban gardens most of them, of course, and the bloom had decidedly gone from most of the ladies present – a case of pruning back hard, I fear.

In the Commons my campaign to become a Vice-Chairman of the '22 Committee started in earnest. I spent the day striding round the lobbies, glad-handing the pathetic handful of smoke-blackened amputees left skulking in the post-Hiroshima landscape that is the modern Conservative Party.

Albany   *Tuesday, 20 May*

Today I called on Messrs Denton Hall & Buggin (est. 1788) of Clifford's Inn in Chancery Lane with a view to pursuing my action against Bradshaw and the *Standard*.

I entered a gloomy Dickensian parlour, where a wizened little clerk was scratching with his quill in a gigantic ledger. He timidly asked if I required young Mr Denton Hall or old Mr Denton Hall. I specified the younger, and was shown into a dark, cobwebby room in which an ancient fellow with half-moon spectacles was

snoring over a large tome about torts. He awoke with a
start, and said that old Mr Denton Hall did not get out
much. I set out my complaint about Bradshaw, and told
him I wished to represent myself in court, at which Mr
Denton Hall quavered, 'Is that wise? Remember how Mr
Kirk Brandon fared against Mr Boy George . . .'

I demanded a writ be served on the *Evening Standard* for
its wrongdoing − namely and to wit, contravention of
Section 84 of the 1988 Copyright, Designs and Patents Act.
I dictated a *stinking* letter, demanding satisfaction. I then
succumbed to a delicious courtroom fantasy in which my
oratory had secured a favourable verdict, and the
forewoman of the jury turned out to be Claire, the New
Labour Member for Watford. Eyes shining, she passed a
note to me from the jury box. A telephone number! Be
still, my fluttering heart . . . !

House of Commons   *Wednesday, 21 May*

A trying day in the House.

The massed choreographed grovelling in Blair's
Stalinist new PMQ left me in a poor humour, and I was
chagrined not to get one of the Vice-Chairmanships of the
'22 − they went to Butterfill,[1] wettish, and Johnson Smith,[2]
a matinée−idol ex−television smoothie. But, thank God, the

---

[1] John Butterfill, Conservative MP for Bournemouth West since
    1983.
[2] Sir Geoffrey Johnson Smith, Conservative MP for East Grinstead
    1965−83; Wealden since 1983. NAC's remark refers to Sir
    Geoffrey's time as a BBC Television reporter in the 1950s.

Chairmanship went to Archie Hamilton,[1] former Min of State at Defence and PPS to the Lady. There may not be much brain there, but at least he is a white man and some approximation of a gent, unlike that silly little gnome MacGregor.[2] The biggest problem we've got in the next five years is not shafting Blair but keeping the Tory party out of the hands of spivs, oiks, drips and men who think White's is a brand of lemonade. Archie is at least a start.

Saltwood   *Saturday, 24 May*

I am sitting in the garden writing this, and the glorious New Labour weather – another bonus feature of the new administration not in the manifesto – continues unabated.

In some ways, I should have been happy to remain up in town over the Bank Holiday, and shoulder the burden of meeting semi-clothed young female constituents in Hyde Park and Kensington Gardens. Instead, I am here at Saltwood, discharging various quasi-feudal obligations. We have just herded a largish group of my local Party workers off the premises. I smartly put down my beaker of mineral water, had the staff tip the half-empty industrial vat of Blue Nun into the moat, opened a bottle of the '83 Pichon-Lalande (experiment later with the '82?) and Jane and I relaxed for the first time today.

Ah, the cares of democracy.

---

[1] Sir Archibald Hamilton, Conservative MP for Epsom and Ewell since 1978.

[2] John MacGregor, Conservative MP for Norfolk South 1974–97 and a former Cabinet Minister.

The Conservative Party continues to skulk like some post–apocalyptic race of underground mutants, waiting until nightfall to scurry through the shattered masonry and denude the corpses of their gold teeth.

We ought to be like the Spartans at Thermopylae, resisting heroically against enormous odds. Instead, we are a despicable rabble. I am still seething about not being elected to the '22 Executive – presumably because these pygmies in Parliament objected to my proposals to let the Lions vote for the Donkeys.[1]

Still, at least attending the '22 Committee meeting meant I missed a dire ceremony at the Royal Borough for our new Mayor, one Edward Hess, who had the temerity to remark upon my absence. With his ugly, simian brow, little Hess does indeed have a look of Rudolf. My revenge on him will be sweet.

Saltwood   *Sunday, 25 May*

I am stunned. The Lady is meeting Blair in Downing Street – the first of a regular series of close encounters, clearly brokered by the oleaginous Powell brothers.[2] Thus will Blair signal his machismo to his adoring nation, and to the EU apparatchiks currently awaiting his virgin presence on the Continent.

And so the Lady bestows her giddy favours on *Blair*,

---

[1] NAC had proposed an extension of democracy in the parliamentary Party.

[2] NAC appears to imply a liaison between Margaret Thatcher's confidant Sir Charles Powell and his brother Jonathan Powell, Tony Blair's Chief of Staff.

that former CND member and veteran of the Michael Foot
'83 intake – while I am set at naught! The newsprint swam
as my eyeballs pricked with bitter tears. Politics and women
can be fickle.

To bestir myself, I swam 20 brisk laps of the moat, the
antifreeze tang of the 'Liebfraumilch' clearing my senses.
Shivering, I towelled myself, dressed, and then wandered
up to the library, where I thoughtfully handled an exquisite
first edition of *Paradise Lost*.

Albany   *Tuesday, 27 May*

My pique has been heightened by the fact that the house
which Jane and I were interested in buying in the
Constituency – Campden Hill Square, just opposite the
Pinters – has been sold by its owner (a rather pleasant
Canadian) to someone else, for £1.9 million.

Now we must go through the fag of finding more
halfway decent properties to look at – and meeting their
owners. A curious business in this neck of the woods,
leading one to imagine oneself in Dubai or Kinshasa.

I see that little twister Chirac, in response to the huge
raspberry he has been given by the French electorate, has
responded by gallantly throwing his ally Juppé to the
wolves.[1] Once again, the French have shown that whatever
integrity they once possessed was speared on the barbed
wire at Verdun. Now they are once more a nation of

[1] The French President, Jacques Chirac, had just removed his
unpopular Prime Minister, Alain Juppé, in order to boost the
popularity of his Centre-Right coalition.

equivocators and collaborators. When I see Chirac's shifty, sweating face, I see that he would be more at home hawking black-market nylons and contraband prophylactics out of the wicker basket on his bicycle.

Here in Westminster, the executed deserters of the First World War are to be pardoned by New Labour and – who knows? – offered counselling. Doubtless the excitable followers of Michael Howard on our side will now demand that they are dug up and shot *again*.

Albany   *Thursday, 29 May*

Today I attended Mass at Westminster Cathedral, the Corpus Christi ceremony, presided over by Cardinal Basil Hume – a moral giant, in my opinion, compared to our Lilliputian tambourine-basher, Carey.

Eriboll   *Friday, 6 June*

Another exhausting week in the New Britain, in which Tony Blair has won the Ashes, the football, the rugby, and for all I know the ladies' doubles at Eastbourne.

Today I made my maiden speech in the Commons, reproving my hateful New Labour Election opponent in K&C for dragging up the Harkesses. Then I intervened in a balls-aching Commons Debate about 'London' – a subject on which our dynamic New Labour executive feels its majority is not high enough to manage without referendum.

I told the House that Max Hastings, editor of the *Evening Standard*, should be given a K for his sterling work on this deeply important issue. Perhaps this bonbon will induce Max to muzzle little Bradshaw and his intolerable travesty of my *Diaries*. If not, my lawyers have instructions to *crush* him.

This morning I had an unsatisfactory strategy meeting with Messrs Denton Hall & Buggin in their Chancery Lane offices.

'We will produce a series of star witnesses in court, proving you have been traduced,' quavered Mr Denton Hall. 'Michael Winner has agreed to testify.'

Long silence.

Eriboll   *Sunday, 8 June*

I see Blair's latest edict is a weekly Question Time for ordinary people. Mandelson will presumably shepherd 20,000 T-shirted sycophants into Wembley Stadium for the mass 'Talk to Tony' fest, so they can quiz the new PM on how wonderful he is, before dancing in formation with little coloured cards which make up a huge picture of the Leader, like the North Korean Olympics.

Albany   *Monday, 9 June*

This has been the grimmest evening of my life.

The leadership campaign has begun with a grotesque

series of 'parties', in which our five nincompoop wannabes
in turn produced field marshal's batons of varying length
and girth from their knapsacks – inviting us to go 'Oooh!'
and 'Aaaah!'

As I sipped the execrable wine, I thought that this was
what the Jonestown massacre must have been like when
the faithful eagerly gulped down mugs of poison in the
steaming jungle. Easily the smallest baton, I fear, belonged
to poor little Michael Howard, whose dire powwow was
convened at Jonathan's house in Lord North Street.

Michael was snarling and muttering into his flute of
sparkling white wine about the terrible 'pipple' who
betrayed him, and 'the little traitor' who 'stabbed him in
the back'. His first act after winning, he hissed, gripping my
elbow, would be to place a noose over his pink little pate
and personally pull the trapdoor lever.

But what hope of loyalty, I wondered, from any of
these people? We are like those intimates of the Führer
who hoped in 1943 to celebrate his 10 years as Chancellor
by presenting him with all the treaties he had signed, only
to realise he had broken all of them.

The worst 'do' was in fact Hague's at the Carlton Club,
which, to my eye, was like some sort of ghastly Stonewall
rally, although I was intrigued to see Miss Julie Kirkbride[1]
turning out for Hague: very attractive, her usual line in
black leather miniskirts replaced on this occasion, I am
sorry to say, by a more demure outfit.

But I reflected that the last young man who attracted
her attention was the sensitive Stephen Milligan.[2] As I left

---

[1] Conservative MP for Bromsgrove since 1997. NAC was enamoured
    of her style of dress.
[2] Conservative MP for Eastleigh 1992–4. He was found dead in
    women's underwear in 1994.

the party, I noticed a single orange in a fruit bowl, and brooded. I do hope that, should the Party repose its ultimate trust in Mr Hague, he has no *surprises* in store for us.

Albany   *Wednesday, 11 June*

I am still digesting the terrifying news. Clarke versus Hague in the final, with Hague almost certainly winning on points.

The party is to be delivered up to the shellsuit-wearing nerds and self-abuse Internet enthusiasts. At least the scribblers of *The Times* did not find out how I voted, and even in the confessional of these pages, I am reluctant to divulge the truth.

I lunched with Bruce and Robert [Cranborne] at the Connaught in a dyspeptic mood. The subject of British Airways' new logos based on African art came up, and our comments were so loud and robust that we were asked to leave.

Eriboll   *15 June*

I have been up since five, watching the deer and avoiding the telephone, which rings incessantly with the snickering lieutenants representing those various spasmoid Lilliputians who wish to lead us over the cliff's edge.

More black comedy has been provided by reading

reports of the Prince of Wales. The muezzin on top of the walls of Highgrove is calling us to devote ourselves to the cause of 'education'.

Pretty rich when we consider his own microscopic intellect and the fact that the only education he ever wished to receive was at the hands of Mrs Parker Bowles, who has now distinguished herself by crashing her car into someone and leaving the scene as fast as her old legs would carry her. If only she showed the same discretion the rest of the time.

Albany   *Monday, 16 June*

New Labour presses on with its plans to criminalise foxhunting.

An awkward position. Despite my views, I promised my constituents I would oppose this legislation, and that is what I shall do. But when the pro-field sports marchers swarm through London on 10 July, it might be as well for me to draw the curtains here and lie low. I shudder at the thought of them gathering outside Albany with their animals baying for blood.

Albany   *Tuesday, 17 June*

Well, old puff-ball Clarke remains ahead by a nose − helped, it must now be admitted, by my vote.

I simply couldn't vote for that repulsive nerd Hague, who anyway seems to have made a royal balls-up of the whole thing. But I am very taken with his lovely and innocent fiancée, Ffion – especially now that young Claire, the new Labour Member for Watford, is so frosty towards me. She has given some sort of interview to the *Sun*, hurtfully saying that her 'dishiest man' is one 'Peter Andre'. Who the fuck is Peter Andre? Presumably some sort of Demos wonk, and intimate of Balls and Mandelson.[1]

The day culminated, fittingly, in Teresa Gorman's performance on *Newsnight* – like some sort of medical video about HRT side-effects in which the Whipless heroine of yore came out for the hated enemy Clarke. God help us all.

Albany   *Wednesday, 18 June*

This morning I held my constituency surgery. It used to be a deeply trying experience in Plymouth, with dreary people in sou'westers shuffling in to whinge about cod. But in K&C there is a much more agreeable class of constituent; no one worth less than £1 million, and nothing less than £6 million in The Boltons. If their drains are ever blocked, it is with caviar.

I had a very enjoyable conversation with someone in which we laughed heartily about the bourgeois New Britons congratulating themselves on their pathetic £1,400 windfall from the Halifax. They will doubtless squander it on stone-cladding their maisonettes and trips to 'Center Parcs'.

---

[1] Ed Balls, senior aide to Chancellor Gordon Brown; Peter
    Mandelson, Minister Without Portfolio.

Later we heard that Redwood has thrown his principles to the four winds and scrambled aboard the Clarke bandwagon, in return for the shadow Chancellor's job – from which vantage point he no doubt expects to plunge his galactic dagger into Ken's vitals. To top it all, the Lady has proved beyond all doubt she has lost the plot by choosing this moment to back Hague. It can only end with her punching her nearest and dearest, like poor, confused Ron in California, who apparently is becoming obstreperous, in his confusion, with Nancy.

But what does it *matter*, anyway? It isn't as if any of these deadbeats is actually going to fight an election. The winner will be a stopgap, an Admiral Dönitz, before the real replacement Führer arrives to launch the Fourth Reich.

I will approach the delicious Ffion, on the pretext that I can broker a deal for Hague with Fat Ken. I will then notice a tear welling up in her eye and gently ask what the matter is. Tremulously, she will lay her head upon my chest and tell me how deeply she has always admired me.

Eriboll   *Saturday, 21 June*

I am in a bate.

Just as I feared, our 'leadership' election has ended in fiasco, and I finally registered my abstention by writing the word '*Balls*' in a neat italic script on the ballot paper.

But that is not the worst of it. Since landing in the soup, Jonathan has insisted on hiding out from the Press up here on the estate and is going about in a kilt and false beard, disguised as a crofter. As I write this, he is striding back and forth in the kitchen practising phrases like 'Och aye hoots mon' and 'Devolution now'.

He is in fairly good spirits and his little eyes lit up at the sight of the Armoured Personnel Carrier I keep in the yard, and my extensive collection of more portable weaponry.

However, there was a tricky moment early this morning when the postman appeared – a young, pink-cheeked man with large glasses and longish hair – and Jonathan started screaming, 'Rusbridger! Fucking Rusbridger!'[1] and grabbed the Bren gun I'd lent him.

For a desperate moment I wrestled with Jonathan while the poor chap cowered in the corner with his letters, and the bloody gun went off, blasting a hole in the ceiling and showering us both with plaster.

'I'll pay for any damage,' said Jonathan sheepishly at last.

With what, pray?

Eriboll   *Sunday, 22 June*

Jonathan is proving tiresome. He is *not* a countryman, and the slightest speck of mud on his Gucci loafers sends him into a sulk. He now stays in his room all day muttering into his false beard and appears only at meals.

He kept us up very late last night at dinner with a rambling and incoherent account of how he had been betrayed. He got through the only three bottles of the '83 I

---

[1] Thought to be a reference to Alan Rusbridger, editor of the *Guardian*, against which Aitken had launched a libel action which had ignominiously collapsed.

keep up here, and once Jane had gone to bed, my heart sank
as I recognised a familiar gleam come into Jonathan's eyes,
as he murmured, 'Is there a "health hydro" nearby, Al?'

After an awful row, I eventually told him about Becky,
a farmer's daughter 17 miles up the road, though she must
be 45 if she's a day. Galvanised, Jonathan borrowed an old
bicycle and pedalled off into the rainy night, his kilt
fluttering.

He reappeared at six this morning, pale, dishevelled,
covered in cuts and bruises, his false beard somewhere up
on his forehead. 'Tricky business, Al,' he said. 'You didn't
tell me she was married. I think I twisted my ankle jumping
out of the window.' He limped up to his bedroom, singing
'I love a lassie' under his breath.

Albany   *Monday, 23 June*

I left Jonathan this morning with strict instructions to help
James with the sheep-shearing. 'Right you are, Al,' said
Jonathan absently, spooning porridge into his mouth, never
removing his eyes from the *Financial Times*. 'Sheep-
shearing. Mmmm. Right-o.'

My heart misgives.

Albany   *Wednesday, 25 June*

My arrival last night at David Frost's summer party was
marred by a ridiculous incident on the way in. Preparing to

park, I took a call on the mobile.

'Al, these *sheep*, these bloody *sheep*. What's the matter with the bloody things? Why don't they just keep still? I've got filth and bits of wool all over my tie. I've had to herd them all into the library just to keep them all in the one place.'

I was so put out by this intelligence that I managed to prang the Bentley with a terrible crunch into the host's Mercedes. Had to turn on the old charm with old Frostie once inside.

'Don't worry about it, Alan, super, good to see you,' he said, but I detected a *froideur*.

The guest-list was the usual *haute* showbiz and politics mix, all of them wanting to know where Jonathan was.

'La Paz,' I told them.

Frostie made a very big show of not minding about the car and, at the end of the party, he directed me out when I had to disentangle my car from his with a metallic groan, which covered the noise of Frostie's grinding teeth.

'Left hand down, super, super, left hand down . . .'

I fear that I shall not be invited back on *Breakfast with Frost*.

Albany   *Friday, 27 June*

I am gazing happily out of the window at the driving rain. It is wonderful for the grass at Saltwood, and keeps the hideous backpackers off the streets.

Only the working classes dislike rain, although I hear from Eriboll that Jonathan is moaning about it, even as he labours on what he expects to be the highly profitable explanations of his conduct for the disgruntled bourgeoisie.

The papers are full of the news that Mandelson has taken full political control of the absurd Millennium Dome: the career equivalent of signing on as Entertainments Officer of the *Bismarck*. His new plan is to rename it the Millennium Experience – like changing Windscale to Sellafield – the 'experience' being that of arriving at a smelly converted gasworks and seeing 30 or 40 of Cameron Mackintosh's dancing inverts recreate *Starlight Express* in an aluminium shed. Why doesn't Mandelson simply set fire to a Kilimanjaro-sized pile of £20 notes before a live television audience?

Shangri-La Hotel, Hong Kong   *Sunday, 29 June*

Much against my better judgment, I have been persuaded to come here and witness the handover, chiefly because it was always bound to be the best party of the year.

Within minutes of arriving, I glimpsed Margaret and Denis, the former scarcely recognisable beneath an inch or so of dead-white make-up, and that staring gaze which is such a sad caricature of her old 'go-bury-yourself-Geoffrey' look which we all so adored when employed upon Howe a decade or two ago.

As soon as we got into Kai Tak, while aching from my travels, I rang the old number of that marvellous masseuse Mai Li, but an almost incomprehensible Sax Rohmer voice announced glacially, 'Mai Li, she letire 1982.' God, the tricks age plays on us all.

I had scarcely sat down to a cocktail at the Mandarin with Alastair when a waiter interrupted.

'Mr Crark,' he hissed. 'Terephone.' He directed me to a phone in the corner.

'Al, it's Jonathan!' said the distant, echoey voice. 'Could you spare half an hour to do a small favour for me? Nip over to the Shan Li bank on Kowloon side, ask for Mr Hi, give the number 45453636216 and pick up a little parcel of Swiss francs he's been looking after for me.'

I hate to be rude to old Jonathan, but I told him pretty brusquely to call Ted [Heath] and get *him* to do it. The old monster would get a thrill from sailing across the bloody harbour.

Shangri-La Hotel, Hong Kong, 4 a.m.   *Monday, 30 June*

Yet another day of shame for Britain, though God knows there have been so many: Prince of Wales with a face like a Victorian mute, Patten[1] appropriately dripping throughout the ceremonies, serried ranks of professional sell-out experts from the Foreign Office and the Lords watching as the bluejackets marched away the gun-carriage carrying the coffin of another chunk of national self-respect.

Albany   *Tuesday, 1 July*

Had to rush back to London before the ink was even dry

---

[1] Chris Patten, Conservative MP for Bath 1979–92; Governor of Hong Kong 1992–7.

on the surrender documents to open some Constituency thing called the Digital Angiography Suite at Cromwell Hospital.

I seized the opportunity to lead one of the white coats aside, and inquire discreetly if they do any special line in flagging sexual drive. But just as he was scribbling down an address, I was handed a message about some awful little local burgher who claims I maltreated him at my Constituency surgery, and 'made him feel like he had just crawled out from under a piece of lino'.

For God's sake. When he turned up at the office I thought he had come to lay the carpet. Then he started whingeing, and I just told him this was a gentleman's Constituency, and if he had any complaints the tradesmen's entrance would be more appropriate. Now he says I was 'rude and arrogant'.

This was the sort of thing one expected in Plymouth, but in K&C – really!

Albany   *Wednesday, 2 July*

Brown's 'emergency Budget' – emergency being the operative word.

As expected, his dour Scots fist, encased in the chain-mail of Envy Socialism, came crashing down on the wealth creators with his windfall tax, in the service of 'welfare-to-work'. 'Welfare-to-bankruptcy-and-grovelling-to-the-IMF' is more like it.

But our own front bench looked pretty pathetic – Lilley wearing his usual apologetic look, and Hague giving the impression he would have been more comfortable in grey flannel shorts. Why is the delicious Ffion committing herself to this man? And what the hell is a 'mortgage'?

Saltwood   *Sunday, 6 July*

Jane and I have spent the evening trying to watch a television programme about the Prince of Wales's weather-beaten paramour, apparently being broadcast as part of an insidious national campaign to bring us out into the Mall in our cheering millions, as she sweeps past in the royal carriage: Queen Camilla.

The moment it had finished, Nick[1] was on the telephone, loyally insisting, 'You have to admit, Al, now you have to admit, she's got marvellous discretion and dignity and really, you know, he does deserve a chance at happiness.'

I was unable to proffer much of an opinion, as the wretched programme was on Channel Five, so I'd had to stand leaning over at 45 degrees by the window with the aerial and it was still a snowstorm.

But I witheringly averred that hosting a few charity lunches for ladies with crumbly bones does not quite excise the public's memory of the two menopausal lovebirds fantasising revoltingly into their mobile phones.

---

[1] Nicholas Soames, Conservative MP for Crawley 1983–97; Sussex Mid since 1997. A former equerry to the Prince of Wales and a close friend of NAC.

Albany   *Tuesday, 8 July*

Today I had to traipse through a hospital and deliver some drivel praising their new angiography machine – whatever the hell that is – finishing off by virtually calling for three rousing cheers for the Brompton Hospital.

Then some snippy little white-coated oik in the audience, obviously bitterly resenting every minute spent away from his private patients in the ingrowing-toenail Bupa suite, sneered, 'This is the Cromwell, actually.'

Actually, it will be the Chelsea branch of McDonald's, to whom I heartily wish the whole thing be sold off lock, stock and barrel.

House of Commons   *Wednesday, 9 July*

This morning I performed *brilliantly* in the House on the subject of the Eurofighter project. It is 'essentially flawed and out of date', I tried to explain to the massed ranks of uncomprehending young New Labour Moonies.

I might as well have been speaking in Swahili for all these people understood of military matters. It is at times like this in the House that I suddenly feel much *older* than everyone else.

Whose spastic idea was the Eurofighter in the first place? Teaming up with the Germans to build fighter planes? Why don't we just apply for an EU grant to build a series of enormous gold statues of Sir Arthur Harris along the Ruhr?

Later, and solely in my capacity as a diarist, I forced myself to attend the preposterous 'Leader's' lunch at the

Savoy, convened by our balding young charisma-bypass patient, Hague.

I strolled up to the River Room entrance on the Embankment, to be dismayed by the sight of the snickering reporters, and of our pathetic troops with their bus tickets and bicycle clips slavering at the thought of their first decent meal in 10 weeks.

I turned smartly on my heel and went up to the Strand, where I tried to find my way through from the main entrance, struggled past the Palm Court orchestra, went up the wrong stairs and found myself by accident at a conference for Essex estate agents. I stuck it for 15 minutes before I realised my mistake.

The luncheon was, as expected, pretty grotesque. Little Hague obviously thought he could boost our morale by telling us to 'work hard and listen hard'. He is clearly unaware of the fact that the only way he could boost our morale would be by attaching a large iron weight to his neck and throwing himself into the Thames. Then perhaps we might get a leader who could come within a country mile of actually *winning* an *Election*.

Albany　　　　　　　　　　　　　　*Thursday, 10 July*

The revolting foxhunters have today descended on the hated townies in Hyde Park for their Countryside Rally, like the pure-minded peasants whom Mao urged to march on the cities to beat up anybody wearing spectacles.

I am in a difficult situation. I have undertaken to oppose anti-field-sports legislation, and yet my sympathies are with the fox, as these awful people know very well.

Albany   *Friday, 11 July*

Decided at the last moment to tough it out at the Huntsmen's Nuremberg in Hyde Park and mingle with the pop-eyed women, claret-featured squires, and their various siblings, spouses, terriermen and unwashed mendicants, who were milling about yelping unintelligibly at each other in the blazing heat, understandably traumatised by their first encounter with London Underground in about 45 years.

It was the biggest gathering since VE Day, but naturally the only way to get it mentioned on the BBC would have been for the majority of its participants to proclaim their unswerving dedication to same-sex acts, while sporting bleached hair and a couple of hundredweight of iron-mongery in their faces. Then at least we would have got on *The Archers*.

Later most of us decamped *en masse* to the *Spectator* garden party, which was a little subdued in these Blairite times.

I noticed a rather seedy figure slouching in the doorway; stubble, frayed cuffs, the sort of chap who hangs around Cairo or Alexandria trying to sell artistic postcards from his overcoat pocket – Lamont.[1] I felt I had to exchange a few words, before fleeing.

Very sad.

Eriboll   *Sunday, 13 July*

We have finally told Jonathan that he will really have to go. Having him lounge around here, outraging the women-

---

[1] Norman Lamont, Conservative MP for Kingston Upon Thames
    1972–97. Former Chancellor.

folk, and talking to his various Omani business associates on the phone all day is becoming intolerable. He has agreed to take a complex series of aeroplane journeys to make it look as if he is flying in from America with his boy.

'We shall be coming in to Paris, Al,' he said smoothly.

'Why Paris, for heaven's sake?' I asked.

'Life goes on, Al, and we all have to make a living,' he twinkled, then suddenly his face darkened with hysterical rage. 'But I won't be talking to those mendacious scoundrels from the newspapers! I shall merely give them a time at which I shall be walking across College Green, with my head held high, and if they wish to photograph me in the course of this blameless activity, that is up to them. But I will not bandy words with them like some bloody silly Buddhist women I could mention.'

House of Commons   *Tuesday, 15 July*

Amongst the callow suburban fashion victims who occupy the Government benches the atmosphere of mourning is comparable to Churchill's state funeral. They have campaigned hard this week for more gay sex – 'equalising' the age of consent at 16. Where will it all end? we ask on this side of the House.

As if in answer, Signor Gianni Versace, purveyor of leather trousers to the Eurotrash classes, dies in a hail of bullets. Now the value of his frocks is going through the roof, but Jane says that when Laura Ashley fell down the stairs the price of our duvet covers stayed the same. There's no justice.

I sense that the sartorial exquisites of New Labour are

sniggering behind my back at the rather short blue knitted
tie that I am wearing today. Cheek.

House of Commons   *Wednesday, 16 July*

To the Park Lane Hotel to launch my forthcoming
television *History of the Tory Party* for the BBC, a ghastly
chore which I have to endure in the cause of publicity, and
to sell my book tie-in.

   Yet again, I have had to explain to the massed uncomprehending teenage reporters my views on how Churchill
should have made peace with the Führer in 1940, and so
saved us a lot of time and money.

   Pa was so good at all this sort of thing, but television
really is very badly paid and so time-consuming and full of
tiresome young men saying, 'Cut! Now, Alan, we need
some kind of stronger entrance from you here, and
favourite is you walking into shot doing something brainy
like holding a book.'

   Afterwards, I turned up to Prime Minister's Questions:
the usual Stalinist farrago, but I found myself seated next to
Marion Roe:[1] a rather handsome woman, not my type
usually, but rather attractive; a definite frisson. Mmmm.

Saltwood   *Sunday, 20 July*

Jimmy has died. On the cards for a very long time, of
course. But the end is always a shock, and I shall always be

---

[1] Conservative MP for Broxbourne since 1983.

grateful to him for not getting one of his poor, benighted Referendum troops to stand against me in K&C.

I doubt if *de mortuis nil nisi bonum* will mean much to the pygmies and chippy salary-men of the newspapers, however, who will snicker at his visionary buccaneering entrepreneurialism: just as they did with Jonathan.

Now his extended family of concubines, mistresses, children and Pakistani cricketers – each with a separate retinue of lawyers – will dispense with the fiction of being on good terms with each other and begin a ferocious battle for Jimmy's cash which will go on well into the next millennium. It will be like the fall of Yugoslavia.

I am more cheered by the news about that Brummie lovely who has long held my poor heart in chains, ever since she objected to the Speaker about my muzzy state in the Chamber after a wine-tasting all those years ago: Clare Short.[1]

I am delighted to see that the Secretary of State for International Development is evidently letting her hair down and enjoying some developments here at home. Some menopausal Labour MP has sheepishly confessed, 'I've been a very silly man with Clare Short.'[2] Sounds to me as if he's been a very sensible man with Clare Short. I would put down a congratulatory Early Day Motion to that effect, were it not that the joyless Cromwellian youngsters on both Government and Opposition benches would take such a dim view.

However, this intelligence has fanned a faint glow into

---

[1] Labour MP for Birmingham Ladywood since 1983. In July 1983, Ms Short complained to the Speaker about the 'condition' NAC was in when he came on to the House after a wine-tasting.

[2] Jim Marshall, Labour MP for Leicester South 1974–83 and since 1987. Thought to have had a friendship with Clare Short.

dormant embers. I am allowing myself the occasional reverie. Perhaps a table for two can be reserved somewhere within earshot of the division bell?

Albany   *Monday, 21 July*

I have returned to Westminster to find little Blair's followers cock-a-hoop and garlanded with flowers because of the latest 'ceasefire' from Sinn Fein: this one being supposedly different from the last one, and indeed the *de facto* 'ceasefire' that obtains between each and every detonation. Having bombed the last Government out of office for being so slow to respond to his demands, Mr Adams clearly believes that Blair will be quicker to obey, especially as David Trimble and his brick-faced farmers now count for less than nothing in the lobbies. Perhaps he is right.

    I have composed a little note to Clare, inviting her to a seminar on new ways of linking aid to trade: irrigation systems in Gabon, tractor parts for Kazakhstan, that sort of thing.

    Wiltons isn't really her, of course, but I thought perhaps a corner table at the Ivy, where we can really thrash out the question of sending wind-up radios out to Borneo tribesmen so they can pick up the World Service. One never knows.

House of Commons   *Tuesday, 22 July*

Why is everyone so obsessed with Welsh devolution,
clearly one of the most balls-aching issues in the world.
Who *cares* if this sly, unlovely people wish to go it alone?

Today, at about a quarter to five, I strode into the
Chamber and was so disgusted to find everyone still
banging on about it that I just turned on my heel and
walked out.

Later, I found a note to call Ms Short's office.
Dangerously excited, my fingers trembling, I dialled. I got
through, not to Clare, but to some smirking little
twentysomething policy adviser called Jessica, who said the
Secretary of State 'thought my suggestions inappropriate'. I
am a little hurt.

House of Commons   *Wednesday, 23 July*

I cannot get used to Blair's new Prime Minister's Questions
starting at three o'clock. I struggled in at about eight
minutes past, assuming I would be early, only to find the
pack in full cry. Most vexing.

Clare was there, of course, in a very fetching flame-red
outfit, the jacket covering some sort of T-shirt-type blouse.
The standard New Labour professional uniform, of course
. . . and yet perhaps it is the fact of its being a uniform that
is so intriguing.

How long can this summer madness continue?

Albany   *Thursday, 24 July*

I see Mandelson has apparently persuaded the Lib–Dems to
refrain from fielding candidates against New Labour in key
constituencies in 2002 – in return for which, poor little
Paddy is allowed to sit in on a few bogus committees so that
in the twilight of his years he can have some pathetic
trappings of Government.

This new Lib–Lab pact is clearly intended to cement
Blair's 1,000-year Socialist Reich. There was a time 20
years ago when our brave and resourceful Security Service
operatives did their utmost to destabilise such a sinister little
pact, thus playing a gallant role in the Lady's triumph in '79
– fitting up Peter Hain on a bank-robbery charge, that sort
of thing. If they had any spunk, our Intelligence chaps
would go into a Barclays Bank in Putney with a sawn-off
shotgun right now, cause a bit of a scene, and then get
someone to point at Hain's picture in the paper and say,
'He did it, Constable.'

But will they? Oh no. Our Blairite Security Services
are probably too busy applying for legal aid to sue their
employers for RSI.

Saltwood   *Sunday, 27 July*

I have been having to rush to every bloody silly Ward
Association party in K&C because some little shit on the
Council has been telling them to put my name on the
invitation. So I have to go or it won't look good. And I
returned to Saltwood in a fine temper to find this letter
waiting for me:

Dear Alan,

Hi. We haven't met since I was elected leader, so I thought it would be good to touch base. As you know, my Fresh Future initiative is all about putting some fizz into the Party, so that we can get back on to the front foot in a very real sense. Basically, we Conservatives need to bond — and how.

So I've hired a little hotel and conference centre in Stevenage for a weekend so that we can all come together — as the late John Lennon would say! — and kick some ideas around. We'll be having presentations and stuff in the morning, but in the afternoon we'll be having softball, bungee-jumping, and most importantly a little paint-ball exercise in the woods to build team leadership and cooperation skills. Lord knows, we need it! It's lotsa fun — we used to do it at McKinsey, taking on teams from Bain, Andersen, and the Boston Consulting Group! I thought you could be a team leader, and I enclose your team leader's red sweatshirt and red baseball cap. Perhaps we could recreate Operation Barbarossa on the Sunday night. What do you say?

Best,
William

If I have anything to do with little Mr Hague's bungee jump, the elastic will, shall we say, lack resilience.

House of Commons   *Monday, 28 July*

Some Smith Square secretary rang this morning: 'Mr Clark, I'm so sorry, we've sent you the wrong sweatshirt and baseball cap by mistake; the red ones should have gone to Mrs Bottomley. We're sending you the yellow ones now.'

She finally replaced the receiver, tearfully protesting that she had 'never heard such language'.

House of Commons   *Wednesday, 30 July*

Lunch today at the Connaught with Robert. He reports that the robust wing of the party is cock-a-hoop about the flood conditions on the Continent and Central Europe being under 20 feet of water. All those sofas and television sets floating away out of upstairs windows on the banks of the Oder basically mean the German economy is more buggered up than ever, making EMU an absolute non-starter!

However, I reminded him that it also meant that in a few years' time the cash calls would be rolling in for those Lloyd's Names on our side still solvent, and come Election time, Weybridge and East Grinstead will reverberate once again to the sound of ropes being thrown over beams and chairs being kicked away.

At this moment, the head waiter said that there was an urgent delivery for Lord Cranborne, and I could see a motorcycle despatch rider carrying a purple sweatshirt and baseball cap.

Not a good week.

Saltwood   *Friday, 1 August*

It is the end of the Half, and I have returned to the country in a holiday humour to find a lot of our local people here very exercised about something called the Love Bus, a rather jolly, brightly coloured vehicle which is apparently touring round the West Country, distributing free 13-year-old girls.

Actually, the whole idea triggered off intense Proustian

longings for the old Love Train up to Scotland. It is all very well zooming up to North Britain in one's powerful Bentley, but it doesn't afford the glorious opportunities of the British Rail Caledonian sex safaris of the Sixties and Seventies. By Watford, I had caught someone's eye. Doncaster saw a nonchalant invitation to dinner in the first-class dining carriage, the brandies would be served en route through Stafford; the insouciant proposal of a nightcap in one's sleeper would come around Crewe, and we slithered into Inverness in a post-coital stupor.

O, les beaux jours.

Saltwood   *Sunday, 3 August*

Excellent news about Robin Cook[1] – the first bit of good news for our side in *such* a long time. This is a much more important boost than our absurdly overplayed victory in Uxbridge,[2] and certainly more than this chippy little business about David Simon's BP shareholding,[3] a matter of two million or so in the Caymans or the Turks and Caicos islands or somewhere like that. I wouldn't notice if I had 'divested' that or not, to use little Hague's spasmoid term.

[1] Robin Cook's relationship with Gaynor Regan had just been revealed, when photographers spotted him taking out a black plastic rubbish sack from her flat.

[2] The Conservatives had just won the Uxbridge by-election, holding on to the seat with an increased majority.

[3] Trade Minister Lord Simon was forced to sell £2 million-worth of shares in his former company BP after Tory complaints that his post as unpaid Minister for Trade and Competition would force him to deal with the oil sector, and lead to a conflict of interests.

Once again, as with Mellor, we are left to wonder at the sheer beneficence of politics: the ugliest men in the world, once in some powerful position, suddenly have Casanova's prerogative to range, rampant, through the West End, on the lookout for younger women — the term being applied technically in this case, as the significant party was 41.

To celebrate, we had a little impromptu Robin Cook theme party here at Saltwood. Alastair [Goodlad], Robert and a few dozen others came down, and Jane ran up some ginger wigs and beards which we all put on, and got thoroughly inspired on '82 Palmer. At dawn, we crept gigglingly outside in our whiskery auburn disguises, each carrying a black plastic bin-liner, and did a ceremonial dance pretending to feed imaginary parking meters. That well-known Ulster knight of the shires, Brian Mawhinney, became particularly overexcited doing it, and fell into the moat — and I had to dive in to fish him out, which put something of a dampener on the festivities.

Albany   *Wednesday, 6 August*

Lunch today with Nick at White's. He is *hopping* about Carey's latest pronouncement on the subject of Charles having to 'choose' between the throne and taking the pungent Mrs Parker Bowles up the aisle.

Apparently, Carey was on some sort of Anglican Fellowship Outreach Conference for Gays in the Northern Territories and some local radio reporter shrewdly offered him a tinnie and encouraged him to say something provocative about HRH. Carey, seemingly unaware of global communication and under the impression that his words would go no further than a dozen or so throwbacks in the bush, obliged.

'Tell me, Al,' boomed Nick in a voice that could be heard on the farthest reaches of the Thames, spraying me with breadcrumbs, 'tell me something, if you will. What the bloody hell has this got to do with him? We had everything tootling along very nicely, everyone gradually getting used to it, even Blair was more or less on board. Then Carey has to mouth off and force our hand. Can't Mandelson get rid of him somehow?'

I'm sure our Minister Without Portfolio can contrive some way of positioning Carey over the trapdoor and pulling the lever.

Saltwood   *Thursday, 7 August*

My loveliest constituent has 'found love' at last, in doing so demonstrating her instinctive knack for doing the thing most likely to give Nick Soames an aneurysm. She has been seen romping with one Dodi (*someone* tell me what it is short for) Fayed, layabout son of the Conservative Party's assassin-in-chief.

I am, of course, hurt. It seems that Diana prefers these Ari Onassis types as being richer and more deferential than our native English stock – as well as less likely to dump to the papers.

And with *bewitching* dumb insolence, she has lighted on the person most likely to infuriate the 'Establishment'. But I fear that once Diana is bored with torturing us in this way, she will find someone less gamey and even richer, and poor Dodi will be dropped like a stone.

I am beside myself. As far as I am concerned, BBC Broadcasting House can be converted into a DIY furniture warehouse. My God, John Birt is a *shit*.

It all began when we had the BBC down here to make my *History of the Tories* television programme. A number of overpaid artistes in slouchy leather jackets swarmed over the place saying tthat such-and-such a location was 'favourite' or 'double favourite'. There was a horrible electricity generator lorry outside that produced a simply *unbelievable* smell and a grotesque catering van dispensing retch-inducing 'butties' from 5.30 a.m.

I had been in their silly little make-up tent for three-quarters of an hour and emerged looking like something from *The Mikado*. I told them that this book is intended to establish my credentials as an *homme sérieux*, not get me an audition at the Palladium.

Next, some invert in a polo-neck sashayed up and said, 'OK, Alan, you just walk into shot and say, "It all started with the Gold Standard dispute in 1925." Then he shouted, 'All right, quiet please . . . quiet . . . Rosalie, my darling, *don't* take the German uniforms away, we're going to need them after lunch . . . Quiet . . . and . . . *action*!'

Then Hanna yelped – my dear little Rottweiler, named after the Führer's test pilot, Hanna Reitsch. The cretinous cameraman, rolling along on some sort of railway track he'd put down on the lawn, had run over her poor little paw.

I suppose she *might* have given the silly man a bit of a nip, because he blubbed and locked himself in one of the caravans, shrieking, 'It's the dog or me, love. I don't need this. I could have had a nice little *EastEnders* run through to December.' Now he's cutting up rough, complaining, and bloody little Birt *won't* come in on my side.

So it looks as if my poor little Hanna might be heading for a Nuremberg verdict at the vet's. If so, I will be adding a completely new chapter to my *History* on Kenneth Baker and his Dangerous Dogs Act.

Albany   *Wednesday, 13 August*

The heat is unbearable; I can't even go away, because I have vowed to do some *constituency work*. Madness. There *is* no constituency work. There is no one here but Norwegian tourists.

Our side's game-plan over the summer is to torture little Mandelson while little Blair is *en vacances*, and see if he can be made to snap. The answer, all too obviously, is yes, but he *loves* doing that; it's what Norman [Tebbit] used to do for us in the Eighties: pantomime-villain routine – draw fire away from the Leader.

Now I see that Diana has taken the hapless Dodi to Chesterfield, deep in Tony Benn country, to see one of her army of gibbering 'psychics' and alternative psycho-therapists. I imagine that Dodi will have to endure a trip to the colonic irrigation clinic – metaphorically at any rate – before this romance is over.

Saltwood   *Sunday, 17 August*

Jane has purchased a gross of absurd electric fans, which we have now put in every room in Saltwood; they just make a noise like a DC-10, and nothing ever gets cool.

Nick has been down here, striding about the garden with a glass of brandy in his hand, gloating over the forthcoming spectacular from the St James's Palace black-propaganda unit.

Apparently our Prime Minister, mustard-keen to suck up to HRH, has got on to this blonde magazine editor in America he knows from his varsity days, who's always getting up in the middle of the night to go jogging. She's placing an article about Charles's gamey old paramour, Mrs Parker Bowles, and the Imam of Highgrove has let it be known that the old girl's chums are to spill some carefully chosen beans.

'Whatever you think about Blair, Al,' said Nick at his customary ear-splitting volume, 'he's very sound on our Great Matter, you know.' Apparently the plan is for the Prince of Wales and his paramour to be seen quietly planting peonies together and worrying about osteoporosis while Diana is involved in an undignified, spitting, face-clawing cat fight with ex-model Kelly Fisher.[1]

'We're winning, we're winning,' sang Nick, capering up and down.

'Perhaps the wedding can be the inaugural event in the Millennium Dome,' I said, a little weary and dyspeptic.

Nick stopped capering, and a misty, awe-struck expression slowly invaded that great, plump face. 'By God, Al, you're *right*!' he said, loud enough to send squadrons of birds screeching out of the trees.

Decisively, I replaced the cork in the brandy bottle.

---

[1] Ms Fisher claimed that Dodi Fayed had broken a promise to marry her.

Albany   *Tuesday, 19 August*

Our side's plan to destabilise Mandelson as much as possible
has had a marvellous boost from that lower-deck lubber
John Prescott, who seems to have about as much say in
Government as he had in the running of Cunard ships when
he was topping up the white wines at the Captain's table.

With his well-known joviality, the Deputy Prime
Minister has compared his colleague to a crab. I hope that
little Blair comes back from holiday before Mandelson's
enormous pincers close round Prescott's throat.

Albany   *Wednesday, 20 August*

I have brought the C-type up to town – 22 minutes, not
bad, bit of a headwind – but got into a slight bate when I
called into my Constituency office to find that some of the
local residents are whingeing tiresomely about a K&C
Council survey, which recommended no changes should
be made to the traffic routes in the area.

The *Bürgertum* of SW3 are clamouring for Limerston
Street to be turned into some kind of spasmoid 'one-way'
system so that the free flow of traffic can be impeded in
order to protect the value of their mortgages. In my
constituents' interests, I solemnly undertook to 'look into'
this deeply important matter directly.

There is a tremendous charge in roaring about the
streets in the C-type, while dreamily appreciating the
summer undress of my young female constituents, as they
celebrate their A-level results. I see, incidentally, that a 15-
year-old girl has been impregnated by an 11-year-old. In

my day, girls tended to be attracted to men four years older.
Now, in Mr Blair's exciting New Britain, the boot is
evidently on the other foot. Nevertheless, what memories
the King's Road brings back from the Sixties, a world of
open-necked shirts and riverside pubs and tennis racquets
slung carelessly on to back seats! I drove up to Beaufort
Street, the inaudible siren song of attraction humming in
my inner ear.

I pulled up outside some sort of coffee bar, where a very
attractive young girl was smiling at me. I swaggered over to
her. As I was about to say something suave, she said, 'Are
you all right, sir? Would you like to sit down?'

The sun went behind a cloud.

Eriboll   *Thursday, 21 August*

I have just received an invitation through the post. It reads:
'The Leader of the Conservative and Unionist Party invites
you to take Loose Johnnies with him in his box at the
Notting Hill Carnival, All Saints Road, W10, Monday
25th August.' On the back, I see that the Leader has done
me the honour of appending a handwritten note:

Dear Alan,
Cecil[1] and I thought it would be kickin' if the local Constituency
MP came and helped out with this one. Ffion and I will be taking
a few photo-calls but we were hoping you could liaise with the local

---

[1] Lord Parkinson, Conservative MP for Enfield West 1970–74;
  Hertfordshire South 1974–83; Hertsmere 1983–92. Chairman of
  the Conservative Party 1981–3 and since 1997.

community leaders at the Mangrove, and maybe you could be a judge for our sound-system competition.

Cecil says that once the dancing starts he's keen to do a bit of 'whining' with the local girls: would that interest you at all? It's very important that we start selling ourselves to the young voters and I think masquerades is the way to it. It'll be a really colourful occasion and I'm trying to get as much of the parliamentary Party down there for the weekend so it really will be a case of all my Tories right here, right now, d'you know what I mean?

William

The answer to this last question is no. The only colour I wish to see at this colourful occasion is the crisp dark blue of the Metropolitan Police uniforms enlivened by the glint of their side-handled batons.

Eriboll   *Saturday, 23 August*

The inhabitants of Montserrat really are being pretty tiresome about their precious volcano, although admittedly this sort of thing can be upsetting. I remember the bonfire we had up here one winter's night about 18 months ago; suddenly the wind changed, and Jane and I and the guests got bits of ash all over us and in the hot punch we'd brought out. It was unpleasant but one bears up.

So far, I see dear Clare Short has been very sound on the whole thing, and I have faxed a memorandum through to her office, pledging my support and suggesting we meet to convene a discreet Montserrat seminar: ecological disasters and the post-colonial context, that sort of thing. The Caprice might be rather nice.

Eriboll   *Sunday, 24 August*

Clare obviously took my memo to heart, and has today
lambasted the Montserratians' latest demand to have a
golden elephant given to each refugee as they saunter into
the Arrivals lounge at Heathrow. Some sort of cultural
thing?

    We are really on the same wavelength on this issue.

    Trembling with excitement, I prepared a position
paper on the Montserrat question, advocating a bold policy
of privatisation and self-help, and have faxed it through to
Clare's office. I telephoned later on, but got that little
twentysomething policy adviser called Jessica, who just
burst into tears and said all communications on this issue
should now be sent to Mr Cook's office.

    My poor Clare.

Kensington Town Hall   *Monday, 25 August*

Christ. I am furious. Smith Square insisted I come to this
wretched Carnival after all; thank God I wasn't photographed, and the papers were more interested in the Leader
and his lovely fiancée sipping unspeakable cocktails out of
coconuts.

    I spent the afternoon hunched inside some godawful
office the party had rented in Ladbroke Grove; the rest of
our pathetic contingent was Mawhinney and little Alan
Duncan,[1] both wearing Hawaiian shirts and sunglasses; they

---

[1] Conservative MP for Rutland and Melton since 1992. Close aide of
    William Hague.

incautiously inhaled next to a gentleman smoking a herbal cigarette the size of a rolling pin and spent the rest of the afternoon giggling and eating Mars bars.

I almost dived for cover when I heard an eardrum-shattering noise like mortar fire; it turned out to be one of the 'sound systems'. Then the Leader shepherded me out into the street, and asked the revellers if they recognised their local MP, and if there was any issue they would 'like to discuss with him'.

This led to rather an ugly scene, and I had to avail myself of a uniformed escort down to safety here.

Never again.

Eriboll   *Sunday, 31 August*

It is as if the sun has been snuffed out, and we are pitched into darkness. What is the Shakespeare line? Had we all but died an hour before this time, then we had lived a blessed time.

When I heard this morning, I was out sailing. I was about to come ashore, when I saw Jane on the bank. She shouted, had I heard the news? I said no, I haven't heard the fucking news, I come up here precisely to avoid hearing the fucking 'news'. But then she called out to me what had happened and I simply came in, and we both went indoors to listen to the news on the wireless.

A car accident, caused by paparazzi – caused by the *Press*. As simple as that. This is pure horror, darkness-at-noon stuff. Never in my blackest moments did I imagine that the prediction I once made in the *Spectator*, that the gutter press would destroy Diana, would literally come true. Spencer has given an interview to the television cameras, saying that the newspaper proprietors who buy these pictures have blood on their hands. He is right, of course.

Jane and I are leaving for London tonight.

Albany   *Thursday, 4 September*

This is absolutely nauseating. The gorge rises at it. The French police have now released the 'information' that the chauffeur was drunk, and, my God, how the newspapers have fallen on it! They are virtually *celebrating*. In their disgusting newsrooms, it is like VE Day. Hooray, hooray, it wasn't us after all. Nothing to do with us. We can go along in the same merry way as before.

And the French authorities are *colluding* with this disgusting whitewash, making bloody sure every scrap of evidence about alleged 'drink-driving' gets leaked immediately to the porcine Fleet Street hacks so that anything to do with French procedural or administrative negligence, or indeed French liaison with British Intelligence (don't tell me they did not have Dodi and Diana under surveillance), is entirely ignored.

Where is the proper inquiry, the proper investigation? Inspector Clouseau will take an aeon before *that* is complete: we shall *never* know how many paparazzi there were, who they were, how they were licensed, whether they had any criminal records. And how many other vehicles were there in the tunnel? And were British Intelligence officers anywhere near? Naturally, any inquiry designed to answer *these* questions will take an age. But anything which suggests that it's all down to one single Frenchman who had had a glass of wine before getting behind the wheel – well, *that* can be released straight away. And my, how the newspapers lap it up. Since hearing this latest item of highly suspect, managed 'news', I have dug out the notes that I made about the Mountbatten case of 1979.

I am *brooding*.

Albany   *Sunday, 7 September*

Well, the funeral passed off peacefully enough, a strange and rather beautiful catharsis to the angry, pseudo-Republican mood that had been building up all week, encouraged, naturally, by the newspapers as another diversionary tactic. (Yes, of course, let us vilify Her Majesty the Queen by all means. It is the obvious course of action, is it not? But stringing up every Fleet Street editor by his thumbs – well, that would be *quite* wrong, naturally.)

The Niagara of hypocrisy is truly revolting, especially from the catch-in-the-throat merchants of the media as they contrive to forget their own culpable role. I expected yesterday to see Mr Romauld Rat, that grotesque paparazzo, solemnly ascend the steps and read a lesson.

When the cortège left Kensington Palace this morning, I mingled amongst my constituents, like an ordinary citizen, though the people parted respectfully in front of me. When the procession turned into Kensington Gore, someone seemed to be taking photographs. A Press photographer. I said out loud, 'Let's string him up,' and the crowd instantly moved to do my bidding. The chap himself turned pale. But with one patrician gesture I stayed the mob's anger, and he was spared.

When the cortège had gone past, I walked back to the flat, and Jane and I watched the rest on television, only finally turning the set off when the limousine, moving along like some large igloo of flowers, turned into Cricklewood High Street on its way up to Northants. The service itself was decent, and Elton John can certainly play the piano. The only false note – and *what* a false note – was Blair reading Corinthians like someone failing an audition for RADA, and doing so in full make-up, eyeliner, pancake, the lot.

A country in mourning, the Monarch humiliated, the national mood ruthlessly manipulated by Mandelson and his focus groupers – and what response is there, in the name of God, from the Conservative Party? The best our baseball-capped Leader can manage is a proposal to rename Luton airport in Princess Diana's honour, perhaps with the erection of a brass plaque in the Duty Free lounge.

It is a relief to look back on happier times for my forthcoming *History of the Tory Party* telly extravaganza, which kicks off next Sunday on BBC2 at 8.30 p.m. I insisted – in the face of the usual whingeing from Corporation Lefties – on interviewing Jonathan. After a good lunch, he slumped down in front of the cameras, and said, 'Well, there used to be a time when the Conservative Party was labelled "the Stupid Party", but I think that was always a bit of a misnomer . . . Look, is there a fee for doing this, Al? I've got to get the next flight back to Oman.'

We shall have to cut that last part.

Eriboll   *Monday, 8 September*

This morning I awoke from a terrifying dream. An

enormous blue lion ridden by the naked Miss Ffion Jenkins was rampaging through the streets of Britain, chasing me. Suitably amended, this might make a rather good title sequence for my programme.

Certainly, the telly is going better than the actual book, which is dragging, to tell the truth. I have my researcher, little Graham Stewart, installed down at Saltwood in Pa's house on the estate and he is hard at work, but even so we shall be pushed to deliver the manuscript on time. Moreover, young Graham is chafing a little about the curfew, but Jane has explained to him that after dark the dogs will dismember any wandering member of the proletariat, so it's for his own good to stay indoors.

This afternoon Alastair telephoned with some astonishing news. It seems that the first of our Defeated has finally got a job, leaving all the other unshaven ex-Tory MPs hanging about outside the dole office, drinking sweet sherry from the bottle and shouting at passers-by. Shiny-pated Michael Forsyth has managed to get his snout in the trough at the merchant bank Robert Fleming, although what use he will be to them or anyone else is a mystery.

Eriboll   *Tuesday, 9 September*

The campaign for 'devolution' up here is building to the most intensely balls-aching climax, the whole thing being a recipe for economic catastrophe north of the Border vigorously promoted by little Blair in order to pay off his gangland Glaswegian supporters at Westminster. But a telephone call from Smith Square has alerted me to the disastrous news that the Lady is coming up here to give a

speech to the Thomas Cook bureau de change annual
dinner-and-dance – for which she has negotiated the usual
fee of her body weight in gold bullion.

'The thing is, Mr Clárk, while she's there she's keen to
throw her weight behind the "No, NO!" campaign, so we
wondered if you could go with her on her walkabouts in
Govan and Sauchiehall Street; we've got the "No, NO!"
rosettes for both of you here, and also the Xeroxed
handouts explaining the Community Charge for you to
distribute.'

I think this is one of those little outings for which our
Armoured Personnel Carrier will be more practical than
the Bentley.

Albany   *Thursday, 11 September*

I positively *shone* at my Press reception at the Carlton Club
today to launch my *History of the Tories* telly programme.
When we finished, I felt like Pavarotti coming off stage at
the Met, flushed, triumphant. Dear Clara [Glynn], our
director, smiled sweetly at me, and I caught sight of myself
in a mirror looking quite 20 years younger. An enormous
wave of *Machtgefühl* courses through me.

Saltwood   *Saturday, 13 September*

We've invited Cecil down for the weekend to watch the
first episode of my *History of the Tories*. He is feeling pretty

low, as apparently the mood in Smith Square is now back at Führerbunker levels, worse than anything under Major and Mawhinney.

'Oh, it's terrible,' he moaned, unconsoled by the '85 Lafite-Rothschild we'd opened. 'He plays this awful pop music in his office and all last week he was bombing on about some new radio station called X-FM and how he just had to be interviewed on it. I promised him I'd see what I could do, and finally told him we'd got him on Radio 2 with Ken Bruce. He got into a frightful bate and stomped off into his office and then that ghastly draper's assistant Duncan stormed in and kept telling me how "disappointed" the Leader was in me. Now his latest idea is to liaise with Pizza Express in naming a new Conservative pizza after the Princess.'

At that moment, the phone rang; Jane answered it and told Cecil it was for him. 'Yes, William, yes,' said Cecil, grimacing at us. 'Anchovies . . . yes . . . black olives . . . no, no, I think jalapeños would be just right . . . optional Diet Coke . . . Jolly good idea, William.'

He returned to the table and poured out another exceptionally large glass.

Albany   *Monday, 15 September*

The papers are *marvellous*.

I am preening myself. Replaying the video of my first episode, I can't decide if I look better outdoors in sunlight, or indoors. I telephoned Clara to ask if we might re-shoot with some more close-ups, but I just keep getting her answering machine. Really, it has to be a Bafta now.

Certainly it was more of a success than our young Leader's catastrophic telly performance yesterday in which he brandished his mace in little Blair's direction, only for it to swing round and bash him on his own hairless pate. I suspect some of my colleagues are beginning to possess just a gleam of understanding that our fortunes would be in quite different shape today with – shall we say – a more mature figure on the podium. Perhaps we should shoot a new sequence, more pointedly addressing the question of leadership. I telephoned Clara to ask about this. Answering machine again.

Albany   *Tuesday, 16 September*

I am beside myself. My brother Colin has seen fit to write some sort of bloody silly autobiography[1] in which he has the intolerable temerity to vilify my motoring enthusiasms and call me 'Toad of Toad Hall'.

He is apparently whingeing about some trifling incident from long ago, when he was in the Porsche with me. He claims I got up a bit of speed driving the wrong way down the Piccadilly bus lane, while supposedly screaming abuse at police pursuit vehicles.

Tosh. We were driving in entirely the correct direction down the Piccadilly bus lane, and I was forced to accelerate a little to avoid the No 4 Routemaster, and then I had to corner fairly smartly round into Lower Regent Street and into Jermyn Street, and then I might have mounted the pavement a tiny bit and went over a little bump which

---

[1] Colin Clark, *Younger Brother, Younger Son*, HarperCollins, £19.99.

might have been a policeman's foot, at which point a Panda car drove up and I might have advised them to target manpower resources at burglary rather than traffic misdemeanours. Fortunately, we outran them in St James's and Ma was able to assure them later that it was probably all just high-spirited varsity chums of Colin's.

But how typical of him to *over-dramatise* everything.

Saltwood   *Friday, 19 September*

We have received through the post a vivid blue envelope marked 'THE FRESH FUTURE STARTS NOW'. Inside is a glossy brochure, showing little Alan Duncan, Sebastian Coe and the Leader on some running track, all in purple shellsuits, crouching in the 'on your marks' position, with the legend 'The race for hearts and minds is about to start!'

Inside, there is a single sheet of paper for our Stalinist referendum. There are two boxes for us to tick. One reads, 'Yes. I support the Leader and his exciting modernisation proposals to take the Party forward into the 21st century.' In much smaller type, there is 'No. I do not embrace the Fresh Future.' The Leader has also appended another of his handwritten notes:

Dear Alan,
I very much hope I can count on your support for this one!
                    William
PS. Our motivational weekend will be at the Eastbourne Grand Hotel, 21–22 October, which is actually in the middle of the week because I am afraid Sebastian cocked up the booking arrangements. Slapped wrists or what!

Anyway, it really will be Pep Central! You will be running Team Leader games in which we'll let you loose in Eastbourne and you have to come back with a policeman's helmet, an astrolabe and an item of ladies' underwear. You'll get your supersoaker in the next post.

Perhaps it is possible to fill this with nitric acid. I have despatched to *The Times* a letter of protest at our Albanian election.

Saltwood   *Saturday, 20 September*

My *Times* letter has generated enormous publicity, and my touch about the election 'not sitting comfortably in our history' has teed up the telly programme very nicely. I telephoned Clara to bring her up to speed about this latest coup, but telling her answering machine isn't the same. Is she ever in?

Saltwood   *Sunday, 21 September*

Another marvellous telly episode, but just as I had decided to open a celebratory bottle of the '79 Petrus, the telephone started ringing as the credits rolled, with whingers objecting to my dashingly radical, revisionist downgrading of Churchill. I expected Robert of all people to admire my line about Salisbury being the last proper toff to lead us. But no.
   'Al, you know I really think you've gone too far this

time,' he chortled uneasily. 'All that stuff about appease-
ment really! And Winston Churchill was a great patrician
leader.'

Nonsense. His mother was American. And just because
my father bought his own castle doesn't mean I'm not a
judge of these things.

Albany   *Tuesday, 23 September*

A discreet lunch today with Jonathan at the Connaught,
discreet because he is supposed to be in America 'writing a
novel' – an absurdly implausible suggestion.

We were both captivated by the news of the nurse
condemned to 500 lashes by the Saudis – because it brought
back wonderful memories of school. 'I wonder, will the
nurse have to carry the beating block out into the Saudis'
equivalent of Upper School and shake hands afterwards?' I
mused dreamily. 'Do they use the cane to twitch aside
one's tails, you know, initially? I suppose they could twitch
aside the flaps of the nurse's *cape* or something.'

'It's not a cane, it's a whip,' said Jonathan through a
mouthful of grouse. 'And the chap has to keep a copy of
the Koran under his whipping arm to soften the blow.
Actually it's pretty lenient, not like taking it from Hurd or
Ferdy Mount.[1] You'd really need a clear, unhindered
whipping action, and at least 700 to warm up.'

'You seem to know a lot about it,' I remarked, and he
went pale and changed the subject.

---

[1] Ferdinand Mount, former head of the Downing Street Policy Unit;
   now editor of the *Times Literary Supplement*.

Albany   *Wednesday, 24 September*

Memorial service today for John Junor[1] at St Bride's, Fleet
Street. Impressive turnout: Denis Thatcher, John Major,
Bernard Ingham, Bill Deedes. Nobody from New Labour
there that I could see. Thank God to attend one occasion
which is safe for white men.

Albany   *Friday, 26 September*

Last night the telephone rang well past midnight, and it was
Jonathan calling on his mobile from the Security Expo 97
in Qatar. He is out there with little Mellor, taking it in
turns to man the Defence Capabilities 'R' Us stand.

'Al! Wonderful news! I have rendered Great Britain a
sovereign service, which frankly shows what a big man I
am, considering the shabby way I have been treated.'

'And what is that?' I asked, wearily, but he seemed
now to have his hand over the phone, talking to somebody
else.

'Yes, Your Highness, 120-millimetre, laser-sighted . . .
well, I'd say a medium-sized town . . . Sorry, Al, what was
I saying? Oh yes – that nurse. Well, I have intervened with
my Government contacts, and I should be able to get her
sentence down to 150 lashes. On certain conditions.'

'And what would they be?'

'Well, she will now have to be naked, but they have,
ahem, agreed that the punishment can be meted out by, ah,

---

[1] Former editor of the *Sunday Express*, and columnist on the *Mail on
Sunday*, who had died in May 1997.

a British national in good standing with the Saudi authorities – er, Your Highness, please don't point that into the crowd. Your Highness, no I really wouldn't press the green button, no don't . . . I'm sorry Al, I'm going to have to call you back.'

Saltwood   *Saturday, 27 September*

We have had Alastair and Robert down here for lunch, and they were both completely white and shaking with rage. The '82 Cos d'Estournel I'd brought up made absolutely no difference.

'I cannot believe it,' said Alastair quietly, clearly on the verge of tears. 'Hereditary peers to be abolished, and the Conservative Party is going to stand by and let this happen.'

'Don't these inexperienced little squits Duncan and Hague understand?' Robert shouted, pounding on the table. 'Soon the people will see through Blair, and they will turn *back* to us, and we shall be *glad* we stuck to our beliefs.'

It is indeed a dark day. This is how it must have felt in Berlin in 1918, when the people were betrayed, their armed forces still striving bravely on enemy soil. I wonder if there is time to re-shoot the final episode of my telly history, calling it 'Stabbed in the Back', mixing black-and-white Weimar footage with shots of Hague? I tried telephoning Clara to ask about this, but her line now actually seems to be out of order.

Saltwood   *Sunday, 28 September*

Another superb episode, though there has been spasmoid whingeing in certain quarters about my forthcoming account of the Lady in next week's climactic edition.

It is, indeed, a daringly revisionist attack on her reputation, and the suggestion that it is in some way motivated by my failure to get into Cabinet is absurd. I was in the library musing on how laughable it was when Jane knocked on the door, saying that she could hear sobbing.

It must be the central heating.

Saltwood   *Wednesday, 1 October*

I am incensed. The *Telegraph* has seen fit to publish some ridiculous attack on me and my telly history, claiming that I am somehow 'pro-Hitler' – a grotesque and illiterate travesty of my argument. Who is this Niall Ferguson anyway? Norman [Stone] says that he is married to a newspaper executive who has the distinction of having been the first person to put the word 'shit' on the front page of the *Sunday Express*.

It really is intolerable that a historian of my standing should be traduced by a *scribbler*.

Meanwhile, I have to decide whether to go up to Blackpool next week for the Party Conference. I think I will succumb. I can bask in some telly fame and, God knows, I have had some happy times at the conference: weaving my magic web all over some nubile young Constituency worker at the absurd but amusing occasions given by Jeffrey Archer.

One year it was a young British Airways stewardess in her charming *uniform* at John King's[1] annual bun-fight, keen to come back to my room to discuss the fall of Crete.

Imperial Hotel, Blackpool   *Monday, 6 October*

Oh, the sheer unmitigated awfulness of it.

We drove up. I couldn't face the terrible rail slog up to Preston, and then having to change on to that dire two-carriage Underclass Soccer Special, where Cabinet Ministers were wont to bash their ankles against the push-chairs of indigent, slow-witted single mothers. One day, the bitter history of the Blackpool Conference's role in rail privatisation will be written (we have apparently handed that line over to beardie Branson for a song). The sea-front is as cold as Poland, and the dismal 'illuminations' have apparently been sponsored by one Eddie Stobart, a haulier of some distinction, featuring – if you please – favourite motorway signs. It was all I could do this afternoon to refrain from flinging myself into the icy gunmetal deep.

Jane and I saw Norman [Tebbit] in the Imperial foyer later, in high good humour after making a vigorous contribution to the debate on multiculturalism – so *vital*, allegedly, for the future survival of the Party. He had claimed that Afro-Caribbeans were not making the effort to be British. I congratulated him on setting a robust agenda for Conference debate; his eyes glowed red and his shimmering grey skin was creased with a sinister smile, like Christopher Lee's when he sees Ingrid Pitt's naked throat

---

[1] Lord King, then Chairman of British Airways.

for the first time.

'Let's see you top that, Alan,' he grinned.

I do love a challenge . . .

Imperial Hotel, Blackpool   *Tuesday, 7 October*

What a wonderful day. I am walking on air. I feel 20 years younger, and Blackpool has never looked more like Cap Ferrat. Quite frankly, Norman can eat my dust.

The day started unpromisingly. A balls–aching 'debate', in the smelly, sepulchral Opera House next to the Winter Gardens, sponsored by the *Guardian* – do we 'stay in the centre ground', or 'go to the Right'? Meaningless gibberish. I was on the platform with Quentin Davies,[1] that Europhile fellow who sounds like Peter Snow, and Patrick Jenkin's boy Bernard,[2] who apparently has a seat these days.

Inviting questions from the floor elicited the usual yelping about Brussels from the woolly–hatted La Tourette's cases in the audience. Then someone asked about our commitment to the SDLP/Sinn Fein/IRA 'peace process' and my blood was up. The memory of a three–bottle lunch in Locket's with Airey Neave in 1975 swam into my head. Over the second port he reached across and gripped my wrist, his face flushed puce, and he produced some sort of Top Secret buff envelope from nowhere.

'It's all in here, Alan! Six hundred names! We know just who they are! We could take them out tomorrow! And it

---

[1] Conservative MP for Stamford and Balding 1987–97; Grantham and Stamford since 1997.

[2] Bernard Jenkin, Conservative MP for Essex North since 1997.

would all be over like that!' and he snapped his fingers violently enough to knock over the cheese board.

So I gave them a gingered–up version of this theory, and that woke them up. Perfectly sound, of course. Surgical strike. Touch of the Führer's Night of the Long Knives: a few clips of nine-millimetre and there you are – no more SA. A frisson ran round the building.

Little Mark Mardell of *Newsnight* oiled up, begging for an interview – but I am too wise a bird to be snared that way. Jane and I were mobbed as we left, but there were some exceptions to the fan club. I exchanged the curtest nod on the way out with Michael Howard, who was sitting with Leon Brittan, John Gummer, and David Waddington – who I'd imagined was still wearing a feathered helmet, superintending the execution of crack addicts out in Antigua or the Bahamas or wherever it is.[1]

Unfortunately, for dinner we could find nowhere better than somewhere called the New Seafood Restaurant in Bond Street. Salmon fishcakes, calamari, chocolate mousse. And the wine list. We had a Pinot Grigio – for £9.25. Not even a decent Montrachet. God help us.

Albany   *Monday, 13 October*

I arrived slightly late for luncheon today with Nick at Wiltons to find him shaking with rage and holding a copy of the Army's new recruiting advertisement. His great puce jowls were positively vibrating with anger.

---

[1] Lord (David) Waddington, former Home Secretary, was Governor of Bermuda 1992–7.

'Explain something to me, Alan, if you will,' he said, in a voice loud enough to make the cutlery rattle. 'Enlighten me, would you? Be so good as to clarify something for me.'

I nodded, and caught the waiter's eye long enough to secure a bottle of the house wine – I'm damned if I'll pay Wiltons' prices to keep Soames in serious claret.

'I see Her Majesty's Armed Forces are trying to attract members of the ethnic community,' Nick bellowed, and then raised both his plump hands. 'I have no quarrel with that. A new intake is needed. From my own experience at the MoD, the CO can count himself lucky just at the moment if his men's literacy skills go anywhere beyond writing the words "Gulf War syndrome" and their solicitor's telephone number.' Here he took up the advertisement again. 'But what I want to know is this. Why was it thought necessary to replace the picture of Lord Kitchener' – and here his voice rose to its customary window-shattering volume – 'with one of a young *Colonel Idi Amin?*'

The times are out of joint in the New Britain.

Albany   *Tuesday, 14 October*

That pitiful oik Merchant[1] has finally bailed out, after some half-baked attempt to double-bluff the tabloids. How very Nabokovian his affair has been. To throw everything away

---

[1] Piers Merchant, Conservative MP for Beckenham 1992–7, was involved before the Election in a tabloid scandal with a teenage club hostess, Anna Cox. He regained the seat, but bowed out later.

on a proletarian clip-joint hostess, that porcine Essex face framed with dyed blond hair, a special sort of mascara that runs easily, the mean little mouth trembling on the brink of tears or some delicious erotic taunt. I wonder if I have space for another research assistant . . . ? Anyway, Merchant's resignation has been the equivalent of a hundredweight of greasy offal dumped in a shark-infested pond.

Portillo called at my set here this morning and excitedly paced the floor. 'Five thousand majority, Alan, ten per cent swing to Blair, but if that little stain Merchant held Beckenham, it means our vote has bottomed out. If you read the *Times* leader column tomorrow, I think you'll find I am not without my admirers. I'm back!' His ramrod-straight carriage and haughty, sensual lips reminded me of a *banderilleros* display Jane and I saw in southern Spain in the Sixties: the imperious matador cruelly protracting the death agonies of a bull heaving about with darts sticking out of its shoulder-muscles.

I asked Michael exactly how this was going to work. He smiled enigmatically. 'I shall carry on being loyal to the Leader's policy with my tolerant, multicultural speeches from the back benches, impeccably supportive right up until the tragically inevitable election result of 2001, ha, ha, ha!'

A hesitant tap on the door heralded a new caller: William Waldegrave. 'I'm not here,' hissed Michael, and he withdrew to the bedroom.

'Should I go for Beckenham, Alan? What do you think?' whinged William. 'You know all about how one goes about impressing a new Constituency Association. Oh, I can't decide. Perhaps I'd be happier with the Wardenship of All Souls . . .'

'Yes, you would,' snapped Portillo, bursting forth. 'I am contacting the Beckenham Constituency Chairman right now.'

'No, I am!'

The two of them then engaged in an undignified running scuffle down the stairs and out into Piccadilly.

Albany   *Wednesday, 15 October*

Last night a dull visit to Kensington Town Hall, to relaunch something called the 'Chelsea Festival'. How very tiresome these Constituency things are. My chagrin has been furthered by reading Bill Deedes's memoirs, in which he harps on his childhood at Saltwood. I regard it as an unpardonable error of taste for the previous occupants to *advertise* themselves in this way.

Saltwood   *Sunday, 19 October*

A wonderful late summer's day. I spent it out in the garden, mowing the lawn, before settling down to reread an interview with one of New Labour's new intake, Miss Lorna Fitzsimmons,[1] who is chafing under the burdens of office: 'I realise that I can't do the things I used to do. I can't have *al fresco* sex, three in a bed, or get totally out of it on drugs.'

Of course it is a *frightful* bore giving up these things when one comes into the House for the first time. I

---

[1] Labour MP for Rochdale since 1997.

remember pining a bit when I came in, in '74, although one soon realises that one can get off the leash sometimes. Miss Fitzsimmons goes on to say, 'There are some men I think, "Cor! Wouldn't mind giving you one!"'

Now I come to think about it, I *have* met Lorna. It was in the Members' Bar one lunchtime and she smiled very attractively at me, and said, 'Oh Alan, I can't get my pager to work; do you know about these technical things?' indicating the small device on her belt. Gallantly, I came forward and was just stooping to examine the offending item, when she suddenly retreated and said, 'Oh, I think it's working again; must dash, I'm on *The World At One*,' and skipped pertly away.

The bewitching little minx.

Albany   *Monday, 20 October*

I met Cecil for a drink at Brooks's early this evening, hoping to talk him into letting me off this absurd bonding session in Eastbourne tomorrow. Wolf once said that nightfall was the most propitious time to try to change someone's mind.

Cecil was actually quite tipsy when he arrived. Apparently, at Smith Square, there had been a day-long party to celebrate 'Brown Monday': a disastrous day which has wiped billions off share prices in the first half-hour of trading.

'Oh Alan, it's been marvellous!' he said happily, having ordered an astringent vodka martini. 'It's such a joy to see the old place *en fête* again, I haven't seen anything like it since the Election night of '83. So exciting. We all crowded into William's office to watch it on television when Brown went into the dealing rooms, and all the little screens went red! There was a tremendous whoop and William and Alan Duncan started dancing to this pop song called "The Only Way Is Up" and then they asked all the secretarial staff to go outside so that we could wave to them from the upstairs windows.' Then, however, it seems that the Leader became thoughtful, his little chin crumpled and he started to blub. 'We will be doing this on election night, won't we, Cecil?'

     Apparently this wretched Eastbourne bonding session is pretty much a three-line whip. No getting out of it.

Grand Hotel, Eastbourne   *Tuesday, 21 October*

A curious day.

     We travelled down on the train, rather fun – a sort of St Trinians-ish feel to the whole thing. I had a very jolly time sitting next to Cheryl Gillian,[1] who wanted to smoke, but someone said it was a non-smoking train.

     'I insist you smoke at this meeting, Cheryl,' I said, my hand brushing her elegantly stockinged knee. 'I shall protect you!'

     'That's not a challenge, darling,' she giggled. She was about to sit on my lap when the carriage suddenly went deathly quiet and cold.

     Hague's trusty Archie Norman[2] had come in, the

---

[1] Conservative MP for Chesham and Amersham since 1992.
[2] Archibald Norman, Conservative MP for Tunbridge Wells since 1997. Former chairman of Asda Group and a close aide of William Hague.

strange former Asda supermarket supremo, his strange waxy face creased in a sinister smile — like some poisoner being led back to the cells.

'Hello, everyone,' he breathed. 'You're enjoying yourselves. Good. But later I shall want you to channel that fun and exuberance into the corporate energy of the political marketplace. I'll be running through it in my first seminar.'

Everyone here seems to have come in informal garb, dressed as they would if they were being photographed by the *People* leaving their mistress's flat at dawn.

Julie Kirkbride is here, I am delighted to say, though not wearing her trademark leather microskirt. She seems to have had her hair done: it's fuller now, softer; it seems to frame her face more becomingly.

There has been no nonsense about paint-guns; it's just photo-calls on the sea-front followed by Norman's balls-aching motivational seminars on how the technique for stacking the tropical fruit counter applies to politics.

Later we were making rather merry in the bar, and Michael Trend[1] sat down at the piano and pretty soon the place was like some sort of gang show, with Peter Lilley singing 'That'll Be the Day', and then Ann Widdecombe belted out a raunchy medley of show tunes from *Hello Dolly!*, until she fell over in the middle of the dance sequence and had to be helped out of the bar.

Finally, I elbowed Trend off the piano-stool and called out, 'Right! I'll give you something really motivational to sing.' I was going great guns until I realised I was the only one singing.

Little Lidington[2] piped up, 'Sorry, Alan, I don't think

---

[1] Conservative MP for Windsor and Maidenhead 1992–7; Windsor since 1997.

[2] David Lidington, Conservative MP for Aylesbury since 1992.

any of us know any German . . .'
    Spoilsports.

Saltwood   *Saturday, 25 October*

This afternoon I was awakened from a light doze by the
telephone ringing.
    'Is that Mr Clark?' Heavy, glottal Ulster accent. I
couldn't place it. 'This is Gerry Adams.'
    I was stumped for a moment, and racked my brains.
'Oh of course,' I said at last, 'the *Thunderbirds* man. *Captain
Scarlet* and so on. The Mysterons. What can I do for you?'
    'No, no, Mr Clark,' said the voice. 'Gerry Adams.
From Sinn Fein.'
    For a second, my blood ran cold. I tensed involuntarily
for the blast, but after a few seconds still heard no sound but
the dulcet Kentish birdsong. Mastering myself, I asked,
calmly, 'How did you get my home telephone number?'
    'Mo gave it to me,' was his reply. 'I was hoping you
might be interested in direct talks to clear the air after your
regrettable remarks in Blackpool.'
    'And where would these talks take place?' I asked icily.
    'Well, Mr Clark, we were thinking of a little pub called
the Beacon in Belfast. It might be just the place for informal
talks and nice photo-opportunity.'
    'Well, I'm not sure if that would be entirely
convenient, Mr Adams,' I said coolly. 'But I have absolutely
no objection to talks in principle.'
    'We could come to you, if you'd prefer, Mr Clark,' he
said, and at that moment I looked out of the window and
thought I glimpsed two black-clad balaclava'd figures

standing in the shrubbery. I dropped the phone and ran outside to confront the trespassers. But there was no sign of them, and the light bruised with nightfall, accompanied by an ominous cold wind whistling through the twigs and branches which formed a lattice across the bleak and racing sky.

House of Commons   *Monday, 27 October*

Our Chancellor has at last condescended to explain his intentions regarding EMU directly to Parliament. He has thus departed from his usual *modus operandi*: devising some equivocal, balls-aching 'policy' with the aid of his teenaged bespectacled wonks and then leaving it to that overweight Communist[1] who used to type out press releases at the AEEU to bully Fleet Street's massed sycophants and dupes into reprinting the Party line.

But what in the name of God is the Party line? As with the Lady and Lawson,[2] it is the old, old story. Number 10 wishes to be seen in the Murdoch prints playing a straight patriotic bat – and is deeply suspicious of Number 11 going native with the Finance Ministers of Europe and selling us out to the Reichsmark.

Brown blustered and stonewalled of course, but Lilley, I fear, did not impress in his reply. Moreover, any head of steam our side could work up was completely deflated by that puff-ball Clarke muddying the water and making trouble with his absurd call for a 'cross-party' initiative on

---

[1] Charlie Whelan, Gordon Brown's influential Press Secretary.
[2] Lord (Nigel) Lawson, a former Chancellor under Mrs Thatcher.

the Euro. If Clarke wishes to take the Hezza path to glory, he should be warned: it leads only to the coronary ward.

Albany   *Tuesday, 28 October*

I ran into Christopher Fraser[1] today in the Lobby. He twitted me about some business luncheon I had missed and a 'delightful' woman who had wished I was there. But I couldn't concentrate. I find myself on tenterhooks. I have allowed myself to be put up for membership of that unspeakably tawdry geriatric ward the Carlton – as a gesture to my new-found seriousness and a testament to the Party I love. Certainly no Party has any love greater than this. That I – who am on the *committee* at Pratt's – should wish to join the Carlton. Frankly, it is *not* smart. In fact, it is notoriously a forum for rather dull provincials. As Balfour told Curzon, 'The Carlton is a beastly club infected by the worst of the species, viz., the bore political.'

Precisely. However, I seem to remember, now I come to think about it, a rather jolly dinner there a few years ago given by the Oxford University Conservative Association, and I had great fun inciting them to devilry. At one stage, old Hailsham was squeaking because we had taken his walking sticks and hidden them in the kitchens. Then we all threw the almond soufflé at the undistinguished pictures, and I persuaded a very sexy girl – Emma, was it? – to steal the Club gavel. It turned up at the House some days later in a shoe-box.

That's the spirit.

---

[1] Conservative MP for Dorset Mid and Poole North since 1997.

Albany   *Wednesday, 29 October*

That smug old hack Wakeham[1] telephoned me at my set here this morning with the supercilious and frankly offensive air of someone who is persuaded against his better judgment to do me a great big favour, ref. the Carlton.

'Tidings of comfort and joy, Alan,' he said smugly. 'We have found space for you.'

'That is very decent of you,' I replied, controlling myself.

'Of course,' he went on, 'some of the members were a little unsure about you. But we managed to bring them round.'

Intolerable. I have a good mind to resign.

Folkestone Magistrates Court   *Friday, 31 October*

The taste of victory is sweet indeed.

We had feared the Goering-at-Nuremberg situation for Hanna: the noblest and most stout-hearted dog imaginable, who has languished on death row for months since the brave beast attacked that hateful BBC man in self-defence.

The secret cyanide pill smuggled into her cell, the last mourning embrace, and then a soft chorus of '*Ich weiss nicht was soll es bedeuten*' together – but quietly, so as not to alert the guards – before Hanna died a Wehrmacht officer's honourable death, thus defeating the contemptible 'medicide' of the Folkestone vet.

But justice prevailed. This absurd BBC man who

---

[1] Lord (John) Wakeham, former Leader of the House of Commons.

claimed to have been bitten, a whingeing cry-baby by the
name of Peter Powell, had described himself in court as
having had experience in Bosnia, Iran and the Gulf.
Experience of what, pray? Dancing the part of Juliet in the
Sadler's Wells touring company? Hanna had given him a
bit of a nip, no worse than a bramble scratch, and he
squealed like a stuck pig. Happily, this ridiculous man had
identified her as Leni. Absurd! They are as distinct as chalk
and cheese! It was a misconception which I was able to
dispute in court with reference to a note I made at the time:
'Hanna was scared by an overpaid corporation functionary
today, who shouted and upset her. God, human beings are
such scum.'

The magistrates could not therefore be sure which dog
was the alleged perpetrator. So Jane and I have emerged
victoriously on the courtroom steps, to acknowledge the
wildly cheering crowds. Not Guilty!

Frankly, I don't think we would have garnered much
sympathetic publicity had it gone the other way. Everyone
here seems to be hysterically distracted by the sinister
moon-faced British nanny Louise Woodward, on whose
behalf we are expected to despatch a gunboat to Boston
Harbour. To some extent, I sympathise. God help any
honest Briton who lands in court in Boston or New York,
where all the judges spend their free time practising their
Riverdance technique.

Saltwood   *Saturday, 1 November*

My brother Colin has dumped in the *Mail,* where he is
parading his personal problems in an absurd 'serialisation' of

his book[1] having obviously been encouraged to do so by the usual convocation of Californian quacks, therapists and colonic irrigation enthusiasts.

I really do wish he would keep them to himself, particularly his impertinent remarks about Papa and about me: 'It's eccentric owning a castle with 15 bedrooms and never having anyone to stay.' What he means is that he is never invited to stay. Mainly because he is now too fat to fit in any of the rooms. I particularly resent his raking up my career at Oxford, and the suggestion that I 'passed on' to him an old girlfriend called Priscilla, in order, as he insists on putting it, to 'break his duck'. I was more interested in breaking his neck.

In fact, Priscilla was a fascinating girl, and our relationship was entirely spoilt by Colin's persistent, oikish overtures. I remember one glorious summer evening in my set at the House, Priscilla and I were reclining intimately on the sofa, and at the crucial moment we heard a supremely irritating spaniel-like scratching at the door – despite the fact that I was sporting my oak – and the sound of Colin whingeing, 'Alan, do you want to come to the Philately Soc? There's a free glass of medium sherry if we arrive before seven.'

Bloody hell.

House of Commons   *Monday, 3 November*

Dinner tonight at the Commons with Nick, who seems to be fuming over some slight from the Speaker. 'Will you

---

[1] See entry for Tuesday, 16 September 1997.

kindly *fill me in* on something, Alan,' he demanded, purple
with vexation. 'I would regard it as a great favour if you
would *brief* me on this. In the Chamber today, I crossed the
floor to chat with a very pleasant MoD civil servant, and
Miss Boothroyd took it into her head to rebuke me, saying
it wasn't done to talk to a "pretty girl". What is she
implying?'

Nick's great, plump features suddenly softened and his
bulging eyes took on a misty, faraway look. 'There can be
nothing between Teresa and me. I am a happily married
man. She is a happily married woman. It could never be.'
In a state of some discomposure, he took a great gulp of
claret.

A highly satisfactory day. It is always a pleasure to take
a slap at Hezza, and today has been no exception. Our
ageing leonine princeling has been inciting the Eurobores
to fight: 'The debate is real and it is going to go on' – the
sort of strident rhetoric that leads to tottering into the air
ambulance wearing a nightie. I gave Hezza a tremendous
smack on the snout. The whingers were out to 'destabilise'
the Leader, I declared, and 'if they don't shut up they
should leave the Conservative Party'. A lovely twirl in the
spotlight for me, and a beautiful statesmanlike gesture. It'll
be ermine in 2001 . . .

Albany   *Monday, 10 November*

This Formula One business really is astonishing. I can't for
the life of me think of a bigger scandal in recent times.

Michael Schumacher has suffered enough. He drives
with panache and style; he drives to *win*, and then he has

the tiniest little prang and this cringing Frenchman or Québecois separatist or whatever he is starts screaming the place down. Perhaps little Jacques Villeneuve would be happier playing mixed badminton.

I used to drive faster than that at Oxford, anyway. I remember rising at 11.50 a.m. during the Hilary Term and betting myself I couldn't make it down to the West End by lunchtime. Ah, those marvellous runs down to town in the SS 100, really letting the throttle out!

I recall a white police van cruising alongside me once, apparently challenging me to make a race of it. Sportingly, I accepted, genially shouting some taunts, and took a swerve just outside Pangbourne and rather cleverly inched him off on to the hard shoulder, losing control of my own car a wee bit, ending up facing the wrong way further down.

Laughingly, I got out and was just about to congratulate the other chap on a jolly good contest, honourable draw and all that, but he cut up *very* rough and the constable in the passenger seat was in tears and seemed actually to be *praying* under his breath. Extraordinary. It took three telephone calls from Mama to square him.

He *looked* a little like Villeneuve, come to think of it.

House of Commons   *Wednesday, 12 November*

This morning's two minutes of silent contemplation for Louise Woodward were rudely interrupted by Colin on the phone, cock-a-hoop about his performance on Radio Four's *Midweek* with Libby Purves. 'She really is *jolly* nice you know, Al,' he bleated. I counselled him to forget it as

Ms Purves is already married, to one of those strange monorchid types who used to work on Esther Rantzen's television programme whining about double-glazing salesmen.

I ran into John Carlisle[1] at the Connaught, a pugnacious little fellow and one of the few members of the Defeated who are now gainfully employed – he is front man for the tobacco growers. Rather *other ranks* of course, but quite amusing and very sound. He was explaining how poor innocent Blair has been taken for a prize idiot by shrewd old Bernie Ecclestone. 'It's marvellous, Alan!' he guffawed. 'Bernie hands Blair a million pounds, gets the tobacco ban revoked – and then *he gets all his money back!*' We roared with laughter.

Over lunch, Cecil reported how the Leader was celebrating the great cigarette victory. 'He and Duncan have bought two of those little mini-racing cars from Hamley's,' he said coldly, 'and they are zooming about his office, doing U-turns. I went in to put a file on William's desk and he bashed into my shins, screeching with laughter.'

A rather carnival atmosphere thus prevailed during Prime Minister's Questions this afternoon in the House, where I cut a statesmanlike figure among the youngsters and miserable old Eurobore malcontents like Hezza and Puff-ball Clarke – men who wear a cologne called Defeat.

I was sitting next to Marion Roe, and near the entrancing Julie Kirkbride – still not wearing much in the way of leather, I am sorry to say. But my mind kept running on my last meeting with Bernie Ecclestone. I was at Silverstone recently, talking politics with Max Mosley, when Ecclestone's *very* attractive wife, Slavica, came up to me. Tall, lovely long dark hair, a black dress made from

---

[1] Conservative MP for Luton West 1979–83; Luton North 1983–97.

about enough material to make a waistcoat for a squirrel. Would I like to have a drink with Bernie and her in their caravan?

I accompanied her to this very odd enormous grey camper-van parked near the track. 'Oh, Bernie isn't here yet, Alan,' said Slavica smiling enigmatically. 'Relax while I change into something more comfortable.' She disappeared, and came back wearing a kind of hot-pants jump-suit, decorated with Marlboro slogans and the Croatian flag. Lithe as a cat, she joined me on the sofa.

'Tell me, Alan,' she purred, passing me a gin and tonic, 'what do *you* think is happening in ex-Yugoslavia?'

I was looking forward to giving her a thorough explanation, when the door banged open and Mr Ecclestone came in, looking like a kind of grey Dudley Moore. 'I see my lady wife is making you feel at home, Alan!' he said cheerfully. 'Now, how do you think I can get through to this Government?' He pondered, thoughtfully fingering a big cellophane-wrapped gift-pack of cigarettes. 'This Sir Patrick Neill[1] – he's probably more of a Dunhill man, isn't he?'

I did not venture an opinion.

Albany   *Thursday, 13 November*

How often have I sent little notes to Miss Claire Ward, the New Labour Member for Watford, proposing luncheon, and how often have these sallies been hurtfully rebuffed.

---

[1] Now Lord Neill of Bladen; Chairman of the Committee on Standards in Public Life.

And yet I return to the fray.

This morning I took it upon myself to fax Claire a briefing, preparing her for the grilling that Hezza was supposed to be getting today about the Dome from the National Heritage Committee (or the Culture and Teletubbies Department, as it is now). I suggested she say to him something like 'The people see a wonderful structure, but they don't know what's going to be in it.' This evening I turned on the news, and there she was, asking exactly that and looking absolutely radiant in an elegant black jacket. She has never looked lovelier: her lustrous hair and rosebud lips enhanced by the electric thrill of political *certainty*.

Who is it she reminds me of?

Albany   *Friday, 14 November*

Nothing goads me more than the sight of that absurd grammar-school boy Edward Pearce,[1] whose balls-aching book about Macleod[2] has been sent to me for review by the *Telegraph*. It is, of course, gibberish from beginning to end.

Pearce is a curious chap. He went to a kind of secretarial college at Oxford and Bruce told me that, when they were both leader-writers on the *Telegraph*, little Pearce wrote that the Battle of Hastings was in 1789 and actually *stamped his foot* when Bruce gently corrected him.

---

[1] Respected parliamentary correspondent for the *Express*.
[2] Iain Macleod (1913–70) was a key figure on the liberal wing of the Conservative Party from the 1950s until his death. He was editor of the *Spectator* 1963–5; Chancellor 1970.

I can never resist taking the lash to Pearce's cringing, supplicant little form. I typed out some lively stuff for my review and sent it off. With any luck, he will rise to the bait and there will be a jolly row.

Saltwood   *Sunday, 16 November*

Jane and I laughed heartily as our Prime Minister delivered his *mea culpa* for the Bernie Ecclestone business on television, having first minimised the time available by banging on about Saddam and the Gulf — a subject on which he is not so much out of his depth as at the bottom of the Pacific Ocean with a weight tied round his neck.

Blair clearly thought that the occasion called for more rouge and powder than normal — more even than for his Diana funeral oration. He looked as if he was auditioning for a part in *Giselle*.

House of Commons   *Tuesday, 18 November*

My long-awaited talks with Sinn Fein took place today,[1] and I have made it quite clear that there is no reason why they should be prevented from taking up their seats in the House.

I decided to take them to Wiltons (for the Irish stew) and it turned out to be rather a good venue. Certainly

---

[1] See entry for Saturday, 25 October 1997.

Gerry Adams seemed remarkably at home and Martin
McGuinness asked if he might have his 'usual table'.

We got through four bottles and McGuinness was on
tremendously good form with stories about the old Europa
Hotel in the Seventies. My estimation of 600 key players
turns out to be a bit generous, incidentally; the subject
made Adams and McGuinness shake their heads
thoughtfully – recruitment problems.

At the end of lunch, while Adams and McGuinness
were cutting their Montecristos and savouring their
digestifs, there was a genial bellow from across the room and
Willie Whitelaw[1] joined us. Soon he and my guests were
chatting away about old times, and I undertook to
campaign for them to be allowed to take their seats in the
House, without taking the Oath. Let no man say that I do
not go the extra mile for peace.

Albany   *Wednesday, 19 November*

Like a laboratory rat trying to detach a piece of cheese from
an electrified wire, poor Pearce has indeed risen to the bait.
He has organised a massed whingers' chorus to join him in
a write-in protest to the *Telegraph*.

It was apparently unforgivable of me to call dreary Iain
Macleod a cardsharper. Is that what I did? I can hardly
remember. The point was to torment the abject Pearce,
who looks exactly like a cringing little fag I used to delight

---

[1] Lord Whitelaw, former Deputy Leader of the Conservative Party,
    and trusted adviser to Mrs Thatcher; former Northern Ireland
    Secretary.

in kicking down the stairs.

However, I was extremely chagrined to see certain other twitching pink snouts appear over the parapet: Patrick Jenkin and *Nick Scott*, excited at the prospect of Clark In Trouble, and moved to write a pompous letter in support of his 'hero' Macleod. No wonder the lionhearted constituency workers of Kensington and Chelsea evicted him in my favour.

But really, it is so childishly easy to get into the papers these days that I can hardly be bothered to do it. I could get out a ruler and measure my column inches – much more than for any of the nobodies and outpatients on what we laughingly call the 'shadow front bench'.

Later this afternoon, I checked to see if there was a note from Claire, acknowledging the flowers. Nothing yet.

Saltwood   *Sunday, 23 November*

Nick arrived for luncheon today, in a bullish humour, direct from a meeting of the St James's Palace black-propaganda unit, which had been in emergency session to discuss the media overreaction to the Prince of Wales's gallant plan to claw back his divorce settlement on his late wife, in order to save himself £8 million-worth of Inheritance Tax.

'Shed some light on something, would you, Al?' he bellowed. 'I wonder if you could account for something to my satisfaction. Why on earth are people being so obstructive about a perfectly straightforward scheme for maximising tax-efficiency? This is *so* upsetting for Wales after all the good press he's been getting lately. He'd even been talking about reactivating Operation Fred and Gladys, but Mandelson thinks it's still too soon.'

Then Jane came in, asking if we'd heard that Michael Hutchence had been found hanged in an Australian hotel room.

'Oh Christ,' groaned Nick. 'Not another by-election. Where was Hutchence, anyway? Swindon? Pretty good majority, was it? For heaven's sake let's get a *married man* next time.'

But Jane said the boys had explained to her that the creature Hutchence was in fact a pop singer, depressed at not being able to see his stepchildren over Christmas. However, the fact that he was stark naked, with his feet touching the ground, would seem to me to indicate the traditional leisure activity of bachelor backbenchers and Anglo-Catholic clergymen.

Or perhaps he had just received a telephone call from Alan Duncan, telling him he had, sadly, not got on to the official Tory candidates' shortlist.

Michael Hutchence might have had interesting views on EMU. We shall never know.

House of Commons   *Monday, 24 November*

A simply glorious day. It seems I only have to lift a finger to dominate the newspapers effortlessly, and completely terrorise this Government of callow spin doctors into the bargain.

---

[1] Alexander Allan, Principal Private Secretary to the Prime Minister 1992–7; High Commissioner to Australia from 1997.

I seem to remember Alex Allan[1] telling me about the fate of Humphrey, the rather charming cat loathed by the Blairs, perhaps because Humphrey was the only non-sycophant on the Downing Street staff.

When Mrs Blair was persuaded to be photographed cuddling him, her awful grimace was due to the fact that poor Humphrey, who suffers from a kidney complaint, relieved himself on her designer outfit just as the shutter clicked. Immediately afterwards, Mrs Blair dropped poor Humphrey with a shriek of disgust and demanded that Campbell do something. Obediently, the Press Secretary produced his laser pen and reduced Humphrey to a mewing pile of ash.

So this morning I demanded that the Government produce Humphrey, and they started running around like headless chickens. Michael Brunson of ITN was driven blindfold to a secret address in Perivale where a cat with approximately similar markings was permitted to be photographed sitting on that day's newspapers like Patti Hearst, though the fact that the papers remained dry should have alerted us to an impostor.

House of Commons   *Wednesday, 26 November*

I bumped into Robert, shaken about an incident in the Lords this morning. Apparently, our newest peer became livid when a 17-year-old female clerk accidentally called him 'Mr' Hattersley and Robert had physically to restrain him as Hattersley brandished his swordstick at her, screaming about 'impudence'.

Prime Minister's Questions was dullish, though it was

nice to be sitting next to Marion Roe again, and she had her right leg crossed towards me today. A definite frisson. We spoke of only one thing: this extraordinary Spencer divorce case in South Africa.

Apparently Spencer's game-plan is to claim that all his money is tied up in the house in Northamptonshire and, by implication, maintaining the sacred Island Shrine itself. Not a bad wheeze, and really one has to sympathise with him. What on earth would this grasping woman want with £3 million, anyway? An ocean of Bailey's, presumably. Enough cash for a second-hand Vauxhall Corsa is surely more than sufficient for her absurd 'needs' and the stout-hearted wise men of the South African bench are bound to agree.

But women from that part of the world can be a delicious snare and I should know, having only with the utmost difficulty extricated myself from the Harkess coven. I must say I have been brooding over press photographs of the lovely young Chantal Collopy[1] and I have only just remembered where I have met her before.

It was in 1980 and I was in Sun City in the sovereign state of Bophuthatswana, on one of those very stimulating R 'n' R weekends that upstanding white man P.K. van der Byl used to organise for sympathetic British Parliamentarians. I was introduced to Chantal at a party. After pouring me some champagne, she plonked herself on my lap with a dazzling smile, and we chatted about estate conservation.

'Ooooh, I do love an English eristocret!' she said in an intoxicating whisper.

Ah, the lost continent of desire . . .

---

[1] A former girlfriend of Earl Spencer.

Saltwood   *Friday, 28 November*

This afternoon I *sparkled* in the House, speaking on the Wild Mammals Bill, which means that if a family goes to a park, and their dog simply chases a squirrel, they get arrested and some Blairite vet with a hypodermic the size of a yard of ale gives the dog the 'Humphrey' treatment.

With my habitual statesmanship, I proposed a compromise whereby the practices of stopping up and digging out are banned. Thus the fox will nearly always win and the element of sport returns.

The elegance of this solution was entirely lost on one Paul Flynn,[1] a Labour man who bobbed up with a whiney intervention about why MoD animal experiments increased after 1992 when 'Clark was Minister'.

With saintly forbearance, I pointed out that this was when I was out of Parliament. But Flynn simply went on to accuse me of being ignorant of parliamentary procedure. Really.

This evening I switched on the television to see if I was on *Newsnight*, but accidentally pressed the button for Channel 4 and found that one Rory Bremner, a snickering comedian of the inevitable Leftist stripe, was essaying 'impressions' of Conservative statesmen.

On the subject of the late Humphrey of Downing Street, he assumed the persona of an elderly man, with a strange, sneering, middle-class drawl: 'If there's any stray pussy in Westminster, I want to know about it' and so on. The studio audience shrieked, and something about this 'impression' was uneasily familiar. Just at that moment, Jane came in and giggled. Apparently, this travesty was supposed to be me. I do not approve of people doing *impressions*.

---

[1] Labour MP for Newport West since 1987.

Albany   *Sunday, 30 November*

I have returned from the country a little early to attend a little intellectual *soirée*, hosted by Jonathan at Lord North Street. An air of melancholy prevailed, especially within the heart of my London tenant, the neophyte Wiltshire countryman Roger Scruton, who gave a daring paper entitled 'Field Sports: radical strategies of resistance'.

Later I chanced upon Jonathan giving brotherly advice to the tiny, plump and disconsolate novelist Michael Dobbs, the man who gave us Francis Urquhart, and who is suffering marital difficulties. His bestseller gravy train has apparently hit the buffers and his screaming wife has jumped out of the driver's cab wearing orange Buddhist robes.

The tearful Dobbs announced to us that she says she is going to be a llama, which I assume is some sort of animal reincarnation thing. Jonathan told me later that it meant Mrs Dobbs, like Jonathan's own lady wife, and so many of a certain age in our circle, has escaped from the brutal realities of her menfolk into the fantasy world of Tibet, Lhasa and the Buddha of eternal light, armed with nothing but a Volvo, a bag of saffron rice and a copy of *Hello!*. Thank God I have never noticed a trace of orange in Jane's wardrobe.

House of Commons   *Tuesday, 2 December*

This pillorying of Geoffrey Robinson[1] really is disgraceful:

---

[1] Labour MP for Coventry North West since 1976, and Paymaster-General in the Blair Government.

the snippy Socialists are whingeing over the fact that he has money in offshore trusts, and is supposed to be closing down this 'loophole' for everyone else. These beardless nincompoops on the Government benches wouldn't know a 'loophole' if it popped up in their breakfast Corn Flakes and said good morning. Presumably, they believe any lawful means taken by an entrepreneur to keep some of his own money is a 'loophole'. And all this over a paltry £12 million in Sark or Paraguay or wherever it is.

Evidently, Geoffrey had had this money invested in a perfectly legal little family trust organised by my old friend Joska Bourgeois, whom I first met in the Sixties in her gigantic lakeside house in Lucerne, with some of the finest pictures in Europe on the walls. I well remember her handsome face illumined by an enigmatic smile as she placed her liver-spotted old hand on my arm.

'Oooh, Alain,' she breathed, 'I always tell you youngstairs. Nevaire buy shares wiz borrowed meurnay, but eef you *meurst*, 'ave a peurnt on IBM.' A curious woman, but shrewd.

It was the purest contemptible spite of this Government to force Geoffrey to make this announcement about Peps, and how anyone with more than £50,000 in a Pep is to have all their money confiscated. What on earth is a 'Pep' anyway?

Later, I tweaked the nose of Donald Dewar during Scottish Questions, by drolly noting that there are 2,000 honest agricultural workers around Eriboll, and yet it is the 82,000 Glaswegian drug addicts who get all the state help. Dewar flustered and blustered, but the House loved it. It is marvellous how I can *play* the House, like a fly-fisherman.

House of Commons   *Wednesday, 3 December*

This Government has decided to ruin the livelihoods of thousands of butchers by banning beef on the bone. As a vegetarian, I am not affected.

But really it's *crazy*. And I hear rumours that Derry Irvine (or Londonderry Irvine as some of us on this side of the House prefer to call him) has taken to wearing heavy scarlet robes and working late at night by candlelight. His lavishly wallpapered apartments resound to his cries of 'I shall make a Star Chamber matter of it, sirrah.' Has the Lord Chancellor sampled too much boeuf bourgignon?

My heart misgives.

Eriboll   *Sunday, 7 December*

We have had Malcolm [Rifkind] up here, God alone knows why, and six months after the terrible day he seems to be suffering from some kind of Delayed Post-Traumatic-Shock Syndrome. He is like those people who are involved in a car accident; immediately afterwards they are perfectly cheerful, but six months later they dress up in women's clothing and spray their local McDonald's with bullets while screaming about their mothers.

Malcolm spent the first few minutes before lunch bravely saying how much he was enjoying life, no more red boxes, time to read and so on, turning up at BHP Petroleum every other Wednesday in return for a couple of hundred thousand pounds.

But it wasn't long before he burst uncontrollably into tears. 'Why, Alan, why? Why don't the people love us any more? Why?'

I refrained from answering that he should speak for himself. Instead Jane poured him another trembling glass of medium sherry, and he managed to pull himself together enough to go into luncheon.

Our other guest was Cecil, who was very animated about the Leader's new idea: to rename the Scottish Conservative Party, because north of the Border the word 'Conservative' goes down like a turd in a punchbowl. Archie Norman has had a team of pollsters hanging about outside Jenners in Princes Street, canvassing various options, and the runners and riders are now as follows: the Scottish Progressive Unionist Party, the Scottish Democratic Party, the Caledonian Business Party, the Glasgow Rangers F★★★ the Pope Party, The North Britain Party, and the Labour Party. Really it's all so *stupid*, and I became rather angry. Why can't we remain true to our beliefs as *Conservatives* and stop apologising for ourselves?

When I had finally calmed down a little at the end of lunch, Malcolm timidly asked what I was up to, and I said I was having lots of fun in the Commons, and he burst into tears again, and Jane had to lead him out. As Nietzsche said, men are not great enough not to feel envy, so they should be great enough not to be ashamed of it.

House of Commons   *Monday, 8 December*

I was in the library this afternoon, in a light doze, when I was awoken by a tiny, dapper figure – Alan Duncan – pulling insistently at my trouser-leg.

'Alan!' he squeaked, presumptuously. 'Has someone

explained to you what the Leader's new game-plan is?'
Mastering my temper, I confessed that no one had, and
Duncan started capering, prancing and practically doing a
sailor's hornpipe around the library with glee. 'We're going
to support the Government!'

'But aren't we supposed to be an effective Opposition?'
I asked.

'No, no, Alan,' he squealed. 'We'll support them on
gouging single mothers on council estates – it will
embarrass Blair with the Labour Left!'

'Of whom there are about two or three left in the
House,' I said drily.

Duncan became rather quiet at this, and asked what I
proposed to buy 'William and Ffion' as a wedding present.
Evidently, their excruciating 'wedding list' is available in
John Lewis's, or British Home Stores or whatever it is.
Some of the items remain unclaimed, and I have a choice
of a 'wine rack' (contains 24 bottles), matching his-and-
hers car coats, an infra-red massage wand, a lava lamp, a
machine for converting unwanted newspapers into
environmentally friendly fuel briquettes, a pair of secateurs,
and three terracotta window-boxes (Christ!). The option of
seven hundredweight of frozen beef ribs for the barbecue
has been withdrawn, following an urgent communication
from Dr Jack Cunningham.

Has the Conservative Party come to this?

House of Commons   *Wednesday, 10 December*

An atmosphere of jubilation now prevails in Parliament,
following the sensational news that the runaway 12-year-

old daughter of some silly agony-aunt woman[1] who writes for the *Telegraph* has been found safe and well, after a search party had been deployed, composed of thousands of officers, police frogmen, and three helicopters.

For the past 24 hours, the New Labour Members of the British *Bürgertum* had been hunched tensely over their radios in the Tea Room, desperate for news, tearfully clutching pictures of their own pampered offspring, whom they have sent to independent schools, ruining themselves in the process.

'Poor little Bink could be anywhere!' they moaned. 'And who knows what sort of strange men she might meet!'

When the news came through that little Bink was safe it was like the Relief of Mafeking. Cotton-rich suits were stained with tears of joy, and an impromptu chorus of 'Candle in the Wind' began in the Central Lobby.

But I must prepare myself now for the great reckoning: my court action against the *Evening Standard*, and their fraudulent mis-use of my good name.

Court 60, The Thomas More Court Buildings   *Monday, 15 December*

I have sifted the evidence; yet I cannot arrive at a judgment as to whom I find the more fascinating: Sinead Martin, our assistant solicitor, or the lovely and quite brilliant Emma Himsworth, junior to my counsel, the portly Geoffrey Hobbs QC, whose unpromising appearance only serves to

---

[1] Anne Atkins.

set off Emma's beauty with more piquancy, like something from Chaucer.

Sinead is quite strict, which I like, with long dark hair and a charming lilt to her voice. Emma sits behind, in wig and gown, frowning prettily over her submissions. I came face to face with little Bradshaw outside the court first thing, and gave an icy, curt nod. I imagine that he had been held overnight in the Paddington Green police cells and hustled in under a blanket. However, I was dismayed that he did not have to appear between two policemen – and no handcuffs. Pure intimidation.

This morning dear old Les Osborne, our porter at Albany, was in the witness box. Salt of the earth, of course, but did he have to wear all his medals and salute quite so much? For luncheon, I took everyone to the Savoy; most unsatisfactory, as the menu had only just arrived when we had to tramp back to the seat of justice. This evening, I confessed to Emma how nervous I was about my cross-examination tomorrow, and asked if I could go through some of the 'material' with her. She nodded eagerly, and I was about to specify a little place over the road, when Hobbs blundered in, slapping me on the back.

'Worried about your evidence, Alan? I can handle this, Miss Himsworth.'

Did I imagine it, or did Emma flush and bite her lip . . . ?

Court 60, The Thomas More Court Buildings   *Tuesday, 16 December*

A glorious day. Was it Churchill who talked about the

elation you feel when you realise the enemy has unleashed his worst weapon at you and you are quite unscathed?

The atmosphere was electric, and I performed brilliantly in the witness box. Time and again their QC, a sadistic gnome called Peter Prescott, lumbered forward with his cudgel, only to stagger backwards with a rapier wound in his heart.

From first to last, Prescott cut an absurd figure like some Marshall Hall caricature,[1] pacing back and forth, his wig and forehead just visible over the bench. He is like a dog we used to have at Saltwood. It was quite sleek with a loud bark, and yet at the first sign of the stick, it rolled on to its back and whimpered pitifully with all four paws quivering in the air.

Frequently, the judge interrupted Prescott's yappings; I maintained insouciant calm. Finally, Prescott accused me of 'sexual vanity' and I replied that self-assessment is difficult, even when doing one's tax returns. The gust of laughter in court was deafening. I retired from the field, the absolute victor. Afterwards I saw Max [Hastings] slinking away, and I could not resist turning to gloat. 'Your man made a balls-up of that!' I chaffed. 'We shall have to see on the day,' he replied priggishly.

Later, Emma came shyly up and said: 'Well done, Alan!' Genially, I suggested a celebration, but then Hobbs's massive form hove into view.

'Celebration, Alan? Excellent! Miss Himsworth, you may go back to chambers to prepare tomorrow's documents.'

Was my imagination in flight, or did Emma cast one longing look back in my direction, lip trembling, as she

---

[1] The barrister Sir Edward Marshall Hall (1858–1927) was renowned as a powerful advocate.

walked out laden with files into the bitter Stalingrad
cold . . . ?

Court 60, The Thomas More Court Buildings   Wednesday,
                                                    17 December

My tail is up today; and with enormous magnanimity I
went up to Bradshaw before the proceedings and said,
'Hello, Peter.' He replied, 'Hello, Alan.'
        Cheek.
        Our expert witness was a fellow called Harry Coen of
the *Catholic Herald* who deposed interminably about
newspaper 'layout'. I was pretty bored throughout all the
expert testimony, to be frank, except when someone called
Trelford[1] appeared – a small, tanned fellow, who I vaguely
remembered claimed to have had some success with girls.
It is a mystery what women could have seen in a man so
lacking in weight.
        The day ended with some tiresome squabble over
earlier testimony, and we must go through one more day
in the New Year, before a judgment is handed down.
        I sense that the hour of ultimate victory is at hand,
when Bradshaw and the great long streak Hastings file
before me into the Versailles railway carriage, heads bowed,
to sign the instrument of surrender.
        Outside the courtroom, Emma approached me,
wreathed in the most delicious smile. I was about to regale
her with some irresistible gallantry, when she breathed:

---

[1] Donald Trelford, diminutive former editor of the *Observer*, now
    teaching journalism.

'James!' and walked straight past me, and engaged little James Mellor, Prescott's pink-cheeked junior, in conversation.

Are there not moments of bitterness even in the sweetest moments of victory?

1998

Chronology

Laughs off the cost of the court action	1 January
Mayoralty of London	3 January
Court action against Bradshaw and the *Evening Standard* resumes	12 January
Victory	22 January
Sympathy for Bill Clinton	27 January
A lecture to the Royal Society of Literature	5 February
Death of Enoch Powell	8 February
Valentine from Shaznay of All Saints	14 February
Millennium Dome plans unveiled	24 February
Living Marxism conference	27 February
Second Countryside Rally	1 March
Party at Associated Newspapers; reconciliation with Max Hastings	10 March
Jonathan Aitken in trouble again	17 March
Letter from Paul Burrell	22 March
Meets Lord Lloyd-Webber	26 March
Defending Alastair Campbell	31 March
Reflections on George Michael	12 April
NAC's 70th birthday	13 April
An attack on Princess Diana	17 April
Relinquishes the idea of running for Mayor of London; meets Jeffrey Archer; considers the past year in Parliament and the future of the Conservative Party	28 April

Zermatt   *Thursday, 1 January 1998*

A wonderfully crisp, clear morning and at 6 a.m. I climbed up to the summit of the Händerhochschweinbühne. I did it in 25 minutes (though I could once do it in 19), moving smoothly up the West Face, easily overtaking a puffing Belgian in his thirties.

God, how gloriously crisp and sparkling the Alpine air is here, like champagne. From the top, I was intoxicated by the dazzling white sweep of the glaciers, the pretty little steepled village of Kollaborateur dotting the lower slope, the sound of a distant cow bell, and further off on the horizon, the pubic mystery of the forest, like something from Grimm.

A profound, joyous feeling of energy and purpose floods through me; I feel that this is the year in which my Secret Project for conquest can be revealed!

But first, my legal action against the *Evening Standard* must be settled. On Monday week we appear again before the judge, and I shall press for the severest possible sentence. How amusing it has been to think of little Bradshaw in his cell at Paddington Green over Christmas. Perhaps that has brought him to his senses: banged up 23 hours a day, 20 minutes' exercise in some high-walled yard, the fetid showers, the ever-present fear of assault – rather like school.

However, I have been nettled at the suggestion bandied about in Brooks's that I am in some way preoccupied with the cost of bringing this action. Why, I have hardly noticed the cost. A gentleman never concerns himself about these things. A quarter of a million? Faugh! Let it go to a million!

Yesterday, in the little village of Denunziant two kilometres away, a local ironmonger was convicted of pilfering – the local *Strafmeister* decreed that his punishment was to be two dozen strokes of the *Lederriemen* across his cringing back in the town square. As I stood in the crowd, and the crack of the strap and the howls of pain rang through the cold air, I was transported in a reverie to the Chancery Division . . .

Now *that's* justice.

Albany   *Saturday, 3 January*

I am back in London with a renewed sense of purpose and energy. One of the rooms here has been converted into a fully equipped Operations Room: an enormous map of the capital, with little lights and flags. My campaign for the mayoralty of London starts here! But when to go public?

As I was interviewing Esther, a promising young potential staff member of my campaign secretariat here at the flat, a knock on the door heralded the wholly unwelcome arrival of Chris Patten. I nervously kicked the door to the Ops Room shut, as Patten gave a strange little bow, his eyes oddly half-closed.

'As we say in the Far East, Alan, if a man waits by the riverbank long enough, a juniper leaf will fall on the smiling face of the tiger.'

After five seconds of awkward silence, I offered him a drink; he returned an inscrutable half-smile. 'I understand you covet the role of Mayor. Maybe I also. You will have no chance; neither will Mandelson, the fool who wears Mickey Mouse ears. But I could offer you the deputy mayorship. Then, when I am finally Party leader, I could get you ermine. But if you make trouble . . . As they say in Xiangkeng Province, when the warlord offers the peasant either a single fish, or being chopped into a million pieces with his scimitar, does not the wise man opt for the fish?'

He bowed and left, padding silently away in what looked like slippers.

'Will there be anything else, Mr Clark?' said Esther expectantly.

But I was thoughtfully silent.

Albany   *Wednesday, 7 January*

The papers have forced my hand: my campaign for the mayoralty has been revealed. And Patten has signed a round-robin letter to the *Independent* with a trace of aged Eurobores. The Leader has nervously identified Patten as the only signatory with anything resembling gonads.

My campaign has clearly nettled Archer who, with much geniality, approached me at the Connaught and presumed to say that we were now 'rivals'. He chuckled, 'It's like a short story of mine about two boys at school —'

I interrupted cruelly, 'I am sorry Jeffrcy — at *school*?' and had the exquisite pleasure of seeing him flinch like a whipped cur.

Then an extraordinary elderly man with dyed blond hair, accompanied by his pert granddaughter, approached me.

'Alan, hi, looks like we're going to be rivals for the mayorship! It's gonna be me and you and Glenda and Jeffrey.' I looked blank. 'It's me! Peter! Peter Stringfellow! I am running for Mayor! You remember — you came to the club once with Nicholas Fairbairn and one of the girls fainted.'

Christ. Who else is going to come out of the woodwork?

There is an eve-of-Agincourt tingle in the air. On Monday afternoon we return to court for the final day of my private prosecution of the *Evening Standard*. This morning I telephoned Mr Hobbs at his set to inform him that I needed some guidance on some legal points. I knew how busy he was but if Emma, his brilliant junior, could run through them here over a light luncheon – poached salmon, some Sancerre – that would be satisfactory.

'My dear Alan, I shall be delighted to come round and explain whatever concerns you. We needn't bother Miss Himsworth.'

Did the iridescent butterfly of fantasy mislead me, or did I hear in the background a faint gasp and then the sound of a young woman's sobbing?

Another glorious day in court although I fear I missed it.

A stimulating lunch with Tristan[1] at the Savoy. We

---

[1] Tristan (now Lord) Garel-Jones, Conservative MP for Watford 1979–97; former junior Minister in the Foreign Office and Deputy Chief Whip.

agreed that Gordon Brown is a shifty, wall-eyed little brute, similar to the type of shouting militant who used to surround my ministerial car when I was at Employment in the Eighties, visiting Clydeside – a razor sewn in the tam-o'-shanter ready for some shipyard punch-up. Delirious with ambition, he has waited until the Prime Minister is safely on tour in the Orient and then produced a dirk from his sporran and plunged it into Tony's back.

His new campaign biography[1] alleges that Blair ratted on an agreement to let him have first crack. Our side's game-plan is to encourage the papers to gush divisively about what a heavyweight Brown is, even though, of course, we all know he is the biggest airhead in the job since Norman Lamont.

After lunch I sauntered up to Court 60 at the reasonable, civilised hour of 4.15 to find that the place was dark and everyone had gone home early. I telephoned Hobbs and he was cock-a-hoop: everything had gone swimmingly.

Verdict next Monday. Will this result, perhaps, be posted on the Internet and little Bradshaw's sentence be limited to the number of days he has already served on remand?

Either way, I have reserved a private room at Wiltons for my Victory Party. A little reminiscent, perhaps, of Wolf's victory dinner planned for Leningrad in 1941 – but I care not. The preliminary guest-list includes Jane, Aspers, Carla Powell, Bob Worcester, Robert [Cranborne], Claire Ward, Norman [Tebbit], and of course Jonathan, who became very emotional when I invited him. 'Alan, you're doing this for all of us,' he sobbed.

Actually I'm rather amused by the notion of inviting

---

[1] Paul Routledge, *Gordon Brown* (Simon & Schuster, 1997).

young Lauren Booth[1] as well, now that she's actually writing a column for the filthy rag – a little like dining with Coco Chanel in occupied Paris.

Then there are the *damages*. I have succumbed to a little reverie as to what to spend them on. Jane is agitating for one of those automatic cleaning devices for the moat. But what is wrong with doing it by hand? It is better for the environment. In any case, I have been lingering dreamily outside Jack Barclay with my eye on the fantastically sexy new Bentley Azure Convertible – my God, the roar of that magnificent turbo-charged 6.75-litre V8 engine while I hurtle through the Highlands, Lauren laughing deliciously at my side and discreetly stroking the walnut veneer and sumptuous leather cocoon, as I turn off in search of a secluded picnic glade.

Ah, the spoils of victory . . .

House of Commons   *Tuesday, 13 January*

I have deliberately stayed away from court today and came to the Commons to offer my wholehearted support to the Foreign Secretary. I find that there is something about him that commands my sympathy and respect.

His disloyal spouse has dumped vindictively to *The Times* and it seems the poor man was not even allowed to use the telephone to dictate his racing-tips column to the Glasgow *Herald* without Dr Cook plucking shrewishly at the receiver because of some ridiculous 'emergency' about blood transfusion. I therefore felt compelled to back Robin

---

[1] Cherie Blair's half-sister, a journalist.

to the hilt, announcing in the House that he should maintain the Iraqi oil embargo, although for some reason there was a certain amount of tittering on our benches at the idea of my upholding the inviolability of sanctions. Robin acknowledged my support with a cool nod, our eyes met and the fellowship of sheer intellect passed between us like a flash of electricity.

'Robin, you old swordsman,' I said afterwards in a spirit of raillery. 'Can't live with them; can't live without them; can't take them round the world at the taxpayers' expense, eh?' Cook coldly turned on his heel and walked off. I fear there is still a little Old Labour chippiness there.

Albany   *Thursday 22 January*

Victory!

The moment of ultimate triumph has an ineffable sweetness, an almost *sexual* discharge of energy. Only those of a really noble and martial spirit can know what it feels like: the rapture at a dashing and well planned raid, completed with dazzling success. Was this how Montgomery felt at El Alamein? Did this intoxicating euphoria rush through General Kurt Student's veins when the courageous Kämpfgruppen took Crete?

I did not deign to go to the High Court yesterday morning, and instead went straight to the Commons. I could hardly settle down. I popped into the Chamber at just after 11, for the Debate about Geoffrey Robinson and that footling matter of offshore trusts, but my pager vibrated almost immediately with a message to call counsel. I rushed out and dialled the number, my fingers trembling with excitement.

'Emma!' I said.

'No, no, Alan,' said a gruff male voice. 'This is Geoffrey Hobbs. Congratulations – you've won!'

I could hear wild cheering and cries of 'Good old Alan!' in the background. From what I could make out from what little Hobbs told me, Mr Justice Lightman took his seat, produced a weighty document and settled a pair of silver-rimmed spectacles on that saintly face. Then, in a stentorian voice he read out the 'Guilty' verdict, and there was uproar. Bradshaw was, in the traditional manner of felons, 'impassive' in the dock while his various common-law wives and feckless teenage children shrieked their vicious threats and abuse from the public gallery. The Clerk of the Court called feebly for order.

Bradshaw was then relieved of his tie and bootlaces by two doughty officers and taken away.

Victory!

But soon the bitterest questions must be asked. Why was I forced to bring this prosecution privately, while the overpaid functionaries of the CPS stood idly by and Bradshaw luxuriated in his legal aid?

I shall call for the offices of the *Evening Standard* to be razed to the ground, like Rose West's house in Gloucester, so that they do not become a grotesque shrine and place of pilgrimage for undesirables. I shall certainly be raising these questions in the House.

I condescended to give an interview to Miss Julia Somerville of ITN, who was very provoking, calling it all a bit of 'fun'. Fun, indeed!

Jane and I then took our legal team for a celebratory luncheon at Simpson's-in-the-Strand, and the entire company of diners burst into a chorus of 'For He's a Jolly Good Fellow' as we came in.

Afterwards, we repaired to Albany for *digestifs*, to find Jonathan hanging about by the door beaming with contentment and joy — evidently in the sort of mood that used to overtake him after a particularly satisfactory weekend at a 'health hydro'. Apparently he had spent all morning at Holy Trinity, Brompton, praying for this result, and rolling around the floor and gibbering with his alpha class of upper-middle-class management consultants and Open Prison graduates. When he heard the verdict on Radio 5 Live, it was like getting 20 Toronto Blessings at once. So he borrowed the bus fare to get over here.

'Al, it was the most empowering spiritual experience of my life. You have taken your buckler of fair play and the trusty sword of truth against the Press, and short of actually seeing Rusbridger incinerated by a lightning bolt, I couldn't have wished for anything more. Any chance of a drink?'

We went in, and I opened the sheaf of congratulatory telegrams and faxes. There was one from the Wagga Wagga Association Football training camp, New South Wales: 'ALAN. HANDSOME. YOU PLAYED A BLINDER. WELL DONE, MY SON. TERRY.'

A fax from Archer read, 'Alan, this is a wonderful moment for us both. I always believed in you. Jeffrey.'

A special delivery from a Harrods van was accompanied by a handwritten note: 'Alan, Mohamed has instructed me to tell you that "you done f***in good". Please accept these vouchers for a 25-second all-you-can-cram-in-your-trolley race through the Food Hall and the Man Shop. Yours, Michael Cole.'

'Alan, you have given hope to us all. God bless you — Gerald Ronson.'

There was another letter, in a plain manilla envelope; the return address was Calle Incognitos 18, Asunción,

Paraguay. 'Your success has given hope to all of us in the Bund. I do hope that you will once again be able to attend our annual dinner and dance, which will be on April 2nd at the Hotel Streichholzer, Graz.'

And then there was a note from the Thatcher Foundation in Cape Town: 'Dear Alan, Mummy said well done, at least I think that's what she said, we didn't find out until well after dinner. Yours, Mark.'

The time has come, perhaps, to set down some thoughts. I am a major Conservative thinker, a man of substance and standing, a man whom the Party desperately needs when it sees that it is being led by someone with the looks and intellectual mien of a young Charlie Drake. There thus comes a moment of destiny, a moment when a man with real vision and leadership skills has to step forward. It would be intolerable if this moment was soured by some sort of impertinent Socialist scribbler. When we have a new leader in 2001, the Party will thank me for taking the action that I have.

Meanwhile, I am walking on air. All of London seems to me rich and vivid with possibility. I was particularly intrigued by something in the papers about a very talented young person called Natasha Walter who has written a book about *The New Feminism*, and how it now welcomes Conservatives. In a spirit of irresistible gaiety, I have sent her a little note, congratulating her on this excellent development, and wondering if she might be free for a small *intime* seminar on the subject: feminism in the next millennium, breaking free of boundaries, Maggie-as-heroine and so on. I thought perhaps Claridge's.

Albany   *Thursday, 22 January*

I have something of a head. The celebration last night at
Wiltons was really very raucous, the wines various and
plentiful and I am a little delicate – though the residual sense
of triumph is a wonderful restorative, a *hum* in the blood.

Half-past seven in the morning was the time at which I
awoke fully clothed in my rooms here and I have simply no
notion of how I got back. With some difficulty I heaved
myself upright, and looked across to see Aspers lying on the
floor at the other end of the room, face down in the full
regalia of a Zulu chieftain: tiger skin, various flints and
daggers suspended on a chain, his mottled hand clutching
some sort of an enormous spear-cum-knobkerrie. He
seemed to be muttering in his sleep and trying to do the
tribal victory dance that he was demonstrating on the table
late last night. Further along, I could see the prone figure
of Richard [Ryder].[1] I could not quite bear to discover
what condition he was in.

The evening had continued to about three, at which
stage Jonathan – who had been very emotional from the
beginning – tried to lead the assembled company in a half-
sung prayer of thanks for this 'deliverance from evil', and
was only stilled when Carla Powell grasped the back of his
neck firmly and pushed his face into the Stilton.

The papers are mostly pathetic this morning, of course,
with the whingeing leaders written by half-wits who have
simply no appreciation of the subtlety and technical
complexity of the action that I brought. However, in a
spirit of magnanimity, I have agreed to grant an interview
tomorrow to young Boris Johnson of the *Telegraph*.

---

[1] Conservative MP for Norfolk Mid 1983–97; former junior Minister
   in the Treasury and Government Chief Whip; now Lord Ryder.

House of Commons   *Friday, 23 January*

I was delighted that young Johnson was able to see the
enormous regard in which I am held here in the House; its
various functionaries and servitors positively queued up to
express their respectful congratulatory sentiments in his
hearing. Our interview was wide-ranging, I am happy to
say, and I was able to convey precisely the sort of radical
thinking and leadership that the Party now needs.

However, just as we were about to begin, the spectral
figure of Norman [Tebbit] appeared.

'Congratulations, Alan! My heartfelt congratulations,'
he breathed with a strange Dickensian eagerness. I
acknowledged his tribute with a measured bow. His face,
which has a shimmering, rainbow-reptilian pallor in the
electric light, was creased with that awful grimace of a
smile. What is Webster's line about the skull beneath the
skin? It conveys at once malice and panic, like Nosferatu's
when he is caught outside the castle at daybreak.

House of Commons   *Tuesday, 27 January*

My God, how one feels for Clinton!

There is a taste, a decided taste, for that sort of woman.
It is a sort of sexual *nostalgie de la boue*. What an exquisite
paradox it is that only the most refined of sensual palates
can really appreciate this rudimentary dish: those porcine,
proletarian features make for an experience that exhales the
subtle yet entrancing aroma of degradation.

Much vulgar comment has been passed about the
specific propensities of the wide-mouthed Misses Paula

Jones and Monica Lewinsky. Only the pathetic self-loathing *Deutschamerikaner* of Washington's crew-cut political classes could torment themselves with the fantasy of one of these sirens 'performing' this 'sex act' on them and then nervously split hairs about whether or not it constitutes adultery. Really, any sort of 'sex act' is wasted on these people.

In fact, I well remember a lively discussion at a Monday Club evening some years ago, in which I invited the company to nominate the woman in public life likely to be the most proficient exponent of this variant bedroom art, and the verdict was unanimous – and rapturous: Alessandra Mussolini, the comely, full-lipped granddaughter of Il Duce himself.

Now the President has defiantly declared his innocence with the narrow-eyed rat-like cunning of a riverboat gambler. Very clearly, the FBI has ransacked Miss Lewinsky's wardrobe, advised the White House that there is no 'DNA-stain' evidence, so it's her word against his. Mr and Mrs Clinton have therefore gone for broke with a brass-necked denial and much whimpering about the trauma suffered by poor Chelsea and Buddy the labrador

Drinks earlier this evening with Cecil, who was cock-a-hoop over his friendly new working relations with the Government:

'Alastair [Campbell] just handed over that awful smug man Martin Bell's legal bill and told us to do our worst! Said Bell was "off message" over Formula One and that this was "useful backbench discipline". He even said he could give me some titbits from the Foreign Office!'

House of Commons   *Monday, 2 February*

Lunch today in the House with Peter (Luff),[1] and Nick
(Soames) joined us later, looking more annoyed than I have
ever seen him about some entirely unfounded allegations
about young boys being made against one of our most
distinguished expatriate men of letters.

'Wales is *very* put out about this Arthur C. Clarke
business,' he boomed. 'Since Van der Post died, he's been
pining away for some sort of fakir figure to be his guru.
This ancient sci-fi johnnie with the tan and the computers
and the villa swarming with houseboys looked like fitting
the bill.'

It appears that Charles was thoroughly looking forward
to tapping him on each shoulder in a special beach
ceremony in Colombo and then settling down for a chat
about information technology, with Sir Arthur dressed
only in a pair of grotesquely brief white shorts.

Naturally, HMG's official position is that Clarke is a
splendid fellow of unimpeachable moral character. But it is
embarrassing and Nick could not quite bring himself to
explain to HRH exactly what has been going on, and now
Charles is going to stomp grumpily and uncomprehendingly
round downtown Colombo's Buddhist temples with a
dozen grinning cabbies driving clapped-out old Ford Anglias
in attendance, all waiting for the inevitable Tamil blast.

Nick is also very annoyed about the new Government
plans to hand over £20 million of Lottery cash for Bobby
Moore's medals. 'That's almost what we got for my grandfather's papers! I mean, this Bobby Moore, wasn't he once
arrested for something?'

---

[1] Peter Luff, Conservative MP for Worcester 1992–7; Worcestershire
    Mid since 1997.

This fact counts for nothing in the forgiving New Britain.

Albany   *Tuesday, 3 February*

Of all people, I ran into Mellor this evening at the Savoy, who was dining with the stern Francis Maude,[1] and his hamster features were distended with gloating over the great Lottery disaster.

'I knew Labour would make a mess of it, I knew it!' he smirked. 'One of the great national institutions, and this Government has dragged it down.'

We were all particularly amused by the spectacle of Peter Davis, our unimpeachable Lottery 'regulator', wading into a punch-up with the photographers prior to collecting his cards from the hapless Secretary for New Labour *Kultur*.

Waiting for a taxi on the Strand later, I was astonished to see an old friend on a large poster: a handsome woman, apparently advertising Wonderbras for the older female. 'Oh my God!' I gasped to myself. 'Pearl Read.'

My mind went back to our last encounter, at the Berkeley Square Ball in 1982, just before the Falklands. Her *décolletage* was similarly prominent, and dear Pearl's charms – richly mature, even then – were enhanced by her extremely emotional mood as she wobbled over from a party of sinister-looking men with cauliflower ears and gold bracelets.

'Oh gawd, Alan!' she breathed. 'Is it war?'

---

[1] Conservative MP for Warwickshire North 1983–92; Horsham since 1997.

'Yes, Pearl,' I whispered roguishly. 'This could be my last night in Blighty.'

'Oh, Alan.'

We repaired to a patch of unlit turf behind the marquee to discuss the South Atlantic situation, but were brutally interrupted after 15 minutes by 'Charlie', a hulking, scarred bruiser, who told Pearl they were leaving for an Essex nightclub, and candidly advised me to make myself scarce.

I wonder if I still have her telephone number?

House of Commons   *Wednesday, 4 February*

Today I forced myself to attend the absurd Debate about the Foreign Secretary's domestic and secretarial arrangements. It really is intolerable that this extremely able man is being pilloried in this way, the snickering being led by that political Titan, Michael Howard.

I sat next to Howard in the chamber; his face was flushed with fanatical hatred as he grabbed my arm and hissed, 'Alan, this is my chance to make these pipple realise that I am back and I am a political player. By God, this shall be the platform for my renaissance and I shall make it my life's work to unseat that loathsome, disgusting little man!'

'Cook?' I asked.

'Hague,' he snarled.

I was really very bored throughout the subsequent fiasco. Mandelson had drilled his timid troops to interrupt and disrupt the proceedings, as poor Michael shouted, at the very top of his slippery Welsh voice, his denunciation of the auburn adulterer's desecration of his high office. There was indeed something of the night about the

Chamber by the time the curtain was lowered on this farce.

Later, during an emergency question on the Lottery, I caused a sensation by fearlessly demanding to know why the Lottery is dominated by a ghastly mob operation like GTech in any case, who keep a gross of horses' heads on permanent stand-by in the fridge.

Once again, the House was enraptured by my effortless parliamentary command. It's something that Blair and Hague simply cannot do. I played the House like a violin; under my touch it sobbed and moaned and sang like an exquisite Stradivarius or a shy young girl. That is real leadership.

Albany   *Thursday, 5 February*

A strained evening, due to having to attend the annual meeting of the Earl's Court Ward in my Constituency – a hideous collection of impoverished menopausal gentlefolk of either sex hunched over copies of the *Daily Mail* in their 'studio apartments' and raddled Australian dentists stupefied with lager.

I had yesterday presented these people with my heart-felt regrets that I did not have the leisure to attend, owing to a pressing subsequent engagement – an invitation to speak at the Royal Society of Literature. Inevitably, they kicked up, and so I judged it expedient to make a token appearance. Really, it was amusing to see how pathetically easily they were cowed. Isn't there a line from Proudhon about the will to obey?

My arrival at the Royal Society of Literature in Hyde Park was therefore delayed, but after an introduction by a woman who apparently writes books about sexual positions I *scintillated* on the subject of diaries. The assembled blue-rinsed ladies responded to my superb timbre, which simply improves and becomes richer with age. Gratifyingly, they gave a full-throated roar of approval whenever I made a disparaging comment about little Bradshaw.

On a whim, I then elicited a general gasp of dismay from my audience by capriciously announcing that I would not be bringing out a second volume of my *Diaries*. Of course, I may yet exercise the prerogative of changing my mind about this decision. Time will tell.

Saltwood   *Sunday, 8 February*

I returned from taking the dogs out this afternoon, to find that Jane had left a message for me to ring Central Office. This I did, and was put on hold for five minutes listening to solemn martial music, followed by the 'Death March'. Then Cecil's voice came on the line, and behind him I could hear seven or eight Peterhouse catamites from the Conservative Research Department keening like Arab women.

'Alan,' said Cecil solemnly, 'Enoch is gone.'

'Gone where?'

'Gone to his reward, Alan; he is gone.' He broke down in choking sobs.

I was carried back to my final encounter with the party's Lost Leader last year at his handsome house in South Eaton Place (how could he afford it?). After dinner, I was talking with Enoch and the Lady and unwisely brought up the subject of Shakespeare's sonnets.

Enoch fixed me with his basilisk glare. 'Do you mean, Mr Clark, the sonnets attributed to the Stratford man?' He then produced a number of anagram charts and cryptograms which demonstrated, at balls-aching length, why Shakespeare could not in fact have written them.

'So who did?'

'It is surely absolutely plain, Mr Clark, quite plain,' quavered Enoch. 'They are the collaborative work of Tony Gubba and Gerald Sinstadt, now employed as commentators on BBC Television's *Match of the Day*.'

'Quite right, Enoch,' said the Lady, before becoming unwell and having to be helped from the room.

House of Commons   *Wednesday, 11 February*

Over lunch in the House today, Nigel[1] told me about this wonderful scene at the 'Brit' pop music awards, at which he was in attendance on a three-line whip from the Leader. The high point came when a bald man in early middle age pranced over to John Prescott's table, dressed in a black leather jacket and a black miniskirt: the sort of person who now dominates the Government back benches, invariably claiming thousands of pounds of public money to take his bearded 'partner' on a fact-finding tour of Guadeloupe. He then emptied a bucket of ice water over the Deputy PM's head to the uproarious amusement of the cocaine-snorting deadbeats nearby. That will teach Prescott to suck up to pop stars.

But I was delighted to learn from Nigel that four of my

---

[1] Nigel Evans, Conservative MP for Ribble Valley since 1992.

loveliest constituents have won an award: All Saints, the entrancing girl group. The captivating little *lapins* have taken their name from the All Saints Road – the home of their recording studio.

Young Shaznay, the singer, called on me at my Commons office last week to talk about her problems with the drains in Westbourne Park Road and poured her heart out.

'I don't know, Alan, sometimes the music isn't kickin', I think we need an older man figure to be our manager, someone like you.'

Arranging my features into an attitude of concern, I suggested dinner at the River Room; she accepted with touching gratitude, and over a bottle of Montrachet we decided she needed 'mentoring'. It is marvellous to know one still has real empathy with one's constituents.

Saltwood   *Saturday, 14 February*

The weather is strangely marvellous; we can feel El Niño blowing hotly across the Kentish countryside. I have actually had to cut the grass here, and the scent always sends obscure hormones raging through my bloodstream.

I have been brooding over the large, heart-shaped card I have received, with the inscription 'I shall Never Ever forget you', which I suspect is from Shaznay. Her obvious infatuation with me is amusing, although it was indiscreet of her to send the card here. Nothing can ever quite extinguish the pleasing quality of Valentine's Day, its strange adolescent longing, its piquant *gaucherie*.

Albany   *Monday, 16 February*

The telephone rang late this evening and for a delicious moment I thought it might be Shaznay with a 'bootie call'. Unfortunately, it was Cecil, who sounded a little gloomy.

'Alan, I wonder if you could come round to Smith Square. I should value your, ah, advice on something.' He sounded worried.

I climbed into the SS 100, and made it round to Smith Square in 11 minutes. I was shown directly into the conference room, and was astonished to find that it had been redecorated entirely in mauve. Mauve walls, mauve floor, mauve ceiling. There was Hague in a mauve sweatshirt, and a mauve baseball cap bearing the words 'Mauve future'. Also in purple were Coe and little Alan Duncan, bustling about, snapping at each other, and piling up pyramids of cellophaned mauve 'information packs' on a table in the corner for tomorrow's press conference.

Similarly attired, and wearing an expression of the deepest woe, was Cecil, who was sitting in one of the auditorium seats, his 'Mauve future' cap a little askew. He was about to hail me when Hague noticed me and said excitedly, 'Alan! Hi! How do you like it? We were inspired by the Pepsi "Blue" campaign. We're hoping that the *Telegraph* will do a special "mauve" edition tomorrow. Basically, our focus groups were telling us that mauve was a really warm and likeable colour. For a while I was thinking beige, but now I've really got behind mauve. These mauve trainers for the youth wing are super.'

'They'd better be,' snarled a bass voice behind me, 'I'm paying for them.'

I turned round to see a bullish and belligerent business-man whom I recognised vaguely, chewing a cigar and wearing an extraordinary 'Florida' shirt.

Duncan trotted up to him, holding out a spare mauve hat. 'Mr Ashcroft! Michael! You're not wearing your –'

'*Get that bloody thing away from me!*'

Later, over drinks in his newly mauved office, Cecil confessed harrowingly, 'It's awful. He's abandoning the torch, Alan, the Conservative torch.' We are apparently down to a shortlist of three replacement icons: a chrysanthemum, a butterfly, and a dolphin. Christ.

House of Commons   *Tuesday, 17 February*

Why are Constituency surgeries *such* uphill work?

Everybody today seemed to want to whinge about this fellow called Rod Gullet, who has apparently been sacked from somewhere: some sort of local hero, possibly a wearisome 'community' leader? How often must I tell these people that I simply cannot take up petty employment disputes with the Home Secretary. I had a constituent like this in Plymouth in the Eighties who was told his dreadlocks would get caught in the machinery on the bleak industrial estate in which he had found employ; he said they were part of his religion. I expect this is something of the sort. Well, if Mr Gullet cares to write to my Constituency secretary, perhaps I can 'monitor' the situation. I can do no more.

This evening at the House I spoke in support of the Foreign Secretary over Iraq. I spoke after George Galloway, and well after Tony Benn – I took particular pleasure in reminding the House that he had said we would never retake the Falklands, that the task force would be turned back!

It was a subject in which I took a special interest: well do I remember in the early Eighties being present with Jonathan and Mellor at a secret demonstration near the Saudi border sponsored by a Solihull firm called Anthrax Surprise. Pretty impressive, and they laid on a splendid luncheon for us afterwards, though the sand got in the foie gras. But worrying for us now, undoubtedly. Saddam has got the very cream of Midlands craftsmanship at his disposal.

Later, I attempted to buttonhole Robin about the strategic realities of the war but he rushed away, muttering something about having to stop off at a petrol station on the way home to pick up some flowers and some Terry's All Gold.

It is terrible how the cares of state are ageing him. Perhaps it is better to be in Opposition in Robin's particular circumstances.

Eriboll   *Sunday, 22 February*

I found myself in Kinlochbervie today, where everyone was in a great state of excitement about next Sunday's trip to London for the mass whinge-in by the foxhunters, agribusiness barbarians, subsidy addicts, and their various craven mendicants.

They are hiring six coaches from this village alone, and Angus, the local blacksmith, became very overexcited: 'Och, Mr Clark, it'll be a grand day out at yon march, and we've got tickets for *Starlight Express* in the evening, ye ken.'

'No, no, Angus,' interrupted a toothless crone. 'That

was sold out. I've got us matinée seats for *Buddy*.'

'What? Why, you useless old –'

'Dinna ye raise your hand to me, Angus, ye'll no' get your knighthood that way.'

This really is an alien country.

Conservative Central Office   *Tuesday, 24 February*

Cecil invited me for a working luncheon at Smith Square and, along with Francis Maude, we watched television coverage of Blair and Mandelson unveiling their 'Dome'. I honestly don't think I have laughed, simply laughed, so much for a very long time.

Really, an *extraordinary* collection of egregious rubbish and Alton Towers nonsense, distinguished chiefly by its utter intellectual and creative nullity and dominated by a transparent giant with no genitals. Perhaps it is this last feature which shows the Dome most clearly as the inspiration of Michael Heseltine.

While we watched, little Francis scribbled busily in his notes, occasionally muttering 'Excellent!' He is i/c Undermining the Millennium and Cecil says our side's game-plan is to brief the newspapers heavily against Mandelson's 'mismanagement' of the Dome, and that more assurances need to be given before our Party irresponsibly exhorts prudent British businessmen to sink their hard-earned cash into ruinous 'sponsorship' undertakings.

With any luck, the whole thing will be a monumental catastrophe, thus giving us a tremendous fillip for the 2001 election. Just before I left, Cecil murmured that 'Chris' would like a meeting about the mayoralty campaign. He directed me through into a strange chamber, perfumed with saffron tea. From somewhere came the soft yet dissonant music of cymbals.

Patten sat cross-legged in a silk dressing gown, giving me that familiar inscrutable smile. He had in front of him a sheaf of manuscript notes of his autobiography, which contains many disobliging references to those Chinese autocrats whose favour the News Corporation so assiduously seeks. He was illustrating it with a delicate watercolour of a hummingbird pecking out one of Rupert Murdoch's eyes.

'Alan,' he breathed. 'If the lion picks up a quill in its paw and writes the story of his life, should he not roar when the fox attempts to take the quill and cross bits of it out?' He stood up and went over to where a brick had been placed on a large plinth. 'I shall attack the fox – like so! Aaaaieee!!'

With a terrifying shriek he brought the side of his hand down in a chopping motion on the brick, which remained intact. Patten placed his hand under his armpit and walked out of the room, bent double. 'Ow,' he said quietly.

I am not certain how useful these meetings are going to be.

Albany   *Wednesday, 25 February*

Lunch today with Eric[1] at the Connaught, and we ran into Tom Camoys, the Palace's new Lord Chamberlain, who

---

[1] Eric Forth, Conservative MP for Worcestershire Mid 1983–97; Bromley and Chislehurst since 1997.

was very downcast at the fiasco of having ushered 'Sir John Elton' into the Queen's presence yesterday.

Apparently he walked forward, knelt, was tapped, and then HMQ just went on and on about how she didn't actually watch television herself, but that her son Edward said that he was frightfully amusing, shouting about 'Thatch' and wearing a spangly suit, and didn't he write novels, and plays as well now, and how she remembered his uncle Sir Geoffrey, the distinguished Tudor historian.

The great entertainer tried to answer as best he could with this awful, fixed smile on his face, and just kept looking daggers at Tom, and then, once he had left and was back out in the corridor, he threw his grey topper on the carpet and jumped up and down on it, making a strange, suppressed yelping noise.

Eric and I got a cab over to the Commons for Prime Minister's Questions, which was the usual dire occasion. The House is uneasy about poor Londonderry Irvine; the House scents blood in the water. He had not yet moved in last May before he started to denude every gallery in Britain of its finest work for his private apartments. So what?

Really, people are so chippy. Surely the Lord Chancellor is allowed to have some halfway decent pictures? Leaving them hanging in Walsall or Glasgow for the benefit of an indifferent and deracinated *Lumpenproletariat* would be quite absurd. They are going to be quite happy trudging around the British Aerospace stalls at the Millennium Dome Dreamscape exhibition, their nylon shell-suits chafing at the thighs. Poussin would be wasted on them.

Albany   *Friday, 27 February*

A glorious day, crisp and cold. The Mall always looks
particularly wonderful in this weather, something to do
with the sheer, vertiginous perspective from Admiralty
Arch to the Palace – unique in London, surely.

But whatever can have possessed me to go there to
speak at something called 'Free Speech Wars'? It was at the
Institute of Contemporary Arts in that rather splendid Nash
terrace, and turns out to have been organised by something
called *Living Marxism* magazine. A ghastly Blairite/
revisionist outfit, of course, but apparently they are
courageously speaking up for the Bosnian Serbs and their
robust struggle to keep Yugoslavia a safe redoubt for Slav
Christianity. (Why are so many of the Left sound on the
Serbs? Some residual attachment to Tito and the Partisans?)
Really, though, what a shower they all were. Hideous
black–clad polytechnic lecturers, homosexual television
producers, and unemployable catamites with dogs on
strings, sporting a hundredweight of ironmongery in their
faces, all screeching interminably about 'free speech' and
the inalienable right to gloat over pornography on the
Internet and yell racial abuse on the football terraces.

Worst of all, there was little Bradshaw, with whom I
exchanged some civil words.

The platform I was on included that appalling blubber
mountain David Banks of the *Daily Mirror*, who published
those grotesque pictures of Princess Diana in a gymnasium.
Thickish. He did not understand how much the newspapers are loathed, and my remarks on this subject were not
readily appreciated by the bovine mob present.

But the editor of *Living Marxism* was a rather charming
young woman, with long dark hair below the shoulders. I
wondered if she had time to discuss my ideas about

protectionism and the limits of the free market, but no, she had to 'rush away' for the next seminar on 'Free Speech for Dictators' with a rubber-importer from Lagos and a former colonel in the Uruguayan Secret Police. A pity.

Saltwood   *Sunday, 1 March*

This morning I was awoken by the sound of a dozen engines thrumming outside. I blearily rose from my bed and went outside to see this hideous, mutinous convoy of hired coaches crammed with people waving banners about standing up to the townie Nazis and all dressed absurdly in green: green wellingtons, green trousers, green waxed jackets. A contrast to their usual garb – protective latex overalls to ward off the effect of the sulphuric acid and paraquat that they spray liberally all over what tiny portion of their fields is not covered by low-level aluminium sheds in which billions of chickens twitch under the glare of neon arc-lights.

Their ringleader, an awful suburban local, appeared to be dressed in hunting pink, though I know for a fact that he has never hunted in his life. He walked up to me, clutching a ridiculous horn, and a placard depicting Lord Donoughue as Julius Streicher.

'Mr Clark,' he said evenly, 'we are giving you one last chance. Are you or are you not going to the Countryside March with the Kent Chapter?'

'Why on earth should I?' I drawled, facing him down.

'Loyalty,' he said.

That was the last straw. 'Hanna!' I shouted. '*Jetzt bist du daran!*' At this signal, Hanna emerged from a side gate, roaring splendidly, and I had the satisfaction of seeing the leader of the Countryside March Kent Chapter gallop back to his 'coach', squealing with fear, with most of his trousers in Hanna's jaws.

Later, Jane and I watched this loathsome mob on television strutting through Trafalgar Square – clearly only about 120,000 or so, but an obvious security hazard. Why on earth didn't the police use their side-handled batons and CS sprays to disperse them?

House of Commons   *Tuesday, 3 March*

Lunch with Cecil and Nick today, and we were all enormously cheered at the prospect of Mr Mohamed al-Fayed having to attend a police station 'voluntarily'.

'It almost makes up for this Rees-Jones nonsense,' growled Nick, who has been greatly exercised by the way Mr Trevor Rees-Jones has been speaking to one of those satanic abuse recovered-memory counsellors for the *Daily Mirror*, with al-Fayed looking on, making soothing noises and encouragingly holding up Rees-Jones's P45.

Apparently Rees-Jones has now remembered that he heard a female voice shouting, 'Dodi!' This, as Cecil pointed out, could easily have been coming from the boot – one of Dodi's female assistants, about whose existence he preferred to remain discreet. Now Mr Rees-Jones has recovered a vivid memory of Henri Paul attending a meeting of fanatically strict teetotallers in a Paris suburb, in full Salvation Army dress, drinking nothing but Vichy water and singing a chorus of 'Shall we gather at the river?'

More revelations are doubtless on the way.

Albany   *Friday, 6 March*

After a terrible, overcooked luncheon in the House today,
I met Karen Buck[1] – a rather charming member of the
Glorious New Dawn Intake of May '97 – who told me all
about an Early Day Motion she wanted to put down,
fiercely condemning tarts' cards in telephone boxes. With
a gallant flourish, I produced my fountain pen and offered
to support this noble cause. Karen melted with gratitude,
and looked on with awe as I dashed off a draft of the
motion on the back of a menu with my customary *élan*:
'This House recognises the offence caused to members
of the public by the extensive use of cards in telephone
boxes . . .' and so on, with effortlessly knowledgeable stuff
about Oftel and call-blocking. By the end, Karen's rather
charming earrings were positively jangling with excitement.

'Oh, Alan!' she breathed. 'It's refreshing to work with
someone who really knows about the House.' Naturally.

I told her I would round up some Tory Members and
Karen sighed in mute assent. And, really, these cards are a
terrible scandal. Not only are they offensive but, simply
from the point of view of consumer rights, they are
deplorable. According to something I read in the *Telegraph*,
the photographs on the cards bear no relation whatever to
the actual product. Apparently, if the Trades Descriptions
Act applied to these cards, they would each read, 'Cheap
and degrading experience in a council flat with someone
who looks like Imelda Marcos. PS: Her violent, crack-
addicted boyfriend might turn up with his Alsatian at any
moment.'

I suggested to Karen that we convene an intimate
seminar to discuss this issue – perhaps the Ivy? She eagerly

---

[1] Labour MP for Regent's Park and Kensington North.

agreed and asked how she should get in contact.

'I have a card here with my number on it!' I said, laughing uproariously, but Karen went oddly quiet.

Perhaps that sally was a little ill-judged.

House of Commons   *Monday, 9 March*

Really, this business about John Prescott is absurd. His office, quite uncontroversially, accepted a donation of some paltry sum. Various malcontents in Mr Prescott's Hull heartland, hanging around the docks, are making trouble about this and some silly housing deal, and now the simpletons of the Press have fainted with indignation.

Honestly, I would hardly notice if I had that trifling amount (£30,000? £300,000? £3,000?). Approximately that much enters my Abbey National Gold Interest Saver Plus account every 55 seconds.

Dinner with Soames this evening at the Connaught was enlivened by the fact that he had come straight from a tempestuous meeting of the Way Ahead Group, which io grappling with the profoundly important issue of whether or not the Duke of Kent should be stripped of his 'HRH'. The meeting was chaired, as ever, by HMQ, and present were Charles, Philip, Andrew, Mandelson, Robert Fellowes,[1] Lord Archer, Anita Roddick, William Rees-Mogg, Lauren Booth and Nick himself. The Group was apparently 'torn' between the Old Guard (Philip) and the Modernisers, with HMQ holding the ring.

'It really is a fascinating debate, Al,' declared Nick in a

---

[1] Former Private Secretary to the Queen.

voice loud enough to shatter glass. 'The Way Ahead group
is developing the ideas that will mould and shape Modern
Britain in the twenty-first century. You know, Al,' he
added, musing into his brandy with a strange, private smile,
'I've always thought of myself as a pretty conservative sort
of fellow. But now I think there might be a case for
equality for *all* members of the Royal Family . . .'

These are exciting times.

Albany   *Tuesday, 10 March*

This evening I went to the very Heart of Darkness:
Northcliffe House, in Kensington – the home of Associated
Newspapers, publishers of the *Evening Standard* – a building
whose threshold I thought I could never bear to cross
again.

This, however, was for a party to celebrate the
publication of a biography of Esmond Rothermere. No
sooner had I walked in through the door, however, than I
was forced to bandy words with little Bradshaw and then I
found myself alongside that long streak Max Hastings. I was
always taught the virtues of condescension in victory,
though myself I have always doubted whether this applies
in white men's wars over lesser races. I muttered a few
gracious nothings to Hastings, though he will have a very
hungry life indeed if he thinks I shall adopt his suggestion
that I should buy him lunch at Wiltons. Really.

After this emotional rapprochement, I felt in need of a
drink and approached someone who had the ruined,
blasted look of an aged servitor, his face and manner
bespeaking a man stooped and coarsened by decades of

material envy and sexual repression. I repeatedly asked for a glass of champagne, and it was only when he kept fingering his bow-tie and talking about how he used to present *Question Time* that I realised I might have made a mistake.

It was the moment for me to take my leave.

Albany   *Wednesday, 11 March*

A visit this morning to the austere, monkish cell of Fr Michael Seed, which lies at the top of a steep flight of stairs in Westminster. I reached the top and tapped uncertainly at the heavy wooden outer door, which lay slightly ajar like a university man's oak.

'Come,' said Fr Michael in a clear, strong voice, and I entered the spare and unforgiving room, in which a narrow single bed reposed in one corner and the occupant himself sat at a fine mahogany desk perusing an early folio volume of St Augustine. The walls were lined with books.

Fr Michael looked up and smiled with enigmatic serenity. 'Mr Clark,' he said softly. 'I knew you would return.'

'Return?' I said, baffled. 'But I have never been here before.'

Fr Michael merely laughed quietly and extracted an exquisite duodecimo from one shelf, bound in calf, endpapers slightly foxed. 'I think this is what you wanted. The *De salute Gregoris* letter from St Pius V. I have marked the relevant passage about animals.'

He opened the book and cleared his throat. 'Shall I translate? "The baiting of bulls and other animals is an abominable custom, bloody and disreputable behaviour worthy of devils rather than men.'"

He looked up. 'A clear moral lead from the Church, don't you agree?'

I was about to reach out and take the book when the door banged open and Ann Widdecombe barged in.

'Ah, Michael,' she barked. 'I think you promised to lend that to me,' and she snatched the book.

Fr Michael only smiled sadly. It appears she takes precedence as a *co-religionist*.

Must I really join the ranks of Miss Widdecombe and little Gummer?

Albany   *Monday, 16 March*

Today Jonathan met me at the Savoy for luncheon, doing a passable imitation of King Lear when Cordelia denies him in Act One.

'Oh God, Al, how sharper than a serpent's tooth it is to have one's children, one's own flesh and blood, disgrace you!' His eyes were wild and hair disordered like some Old Testament patriarch's.

'I was telephoned today to be told that *my daughter Victoria* had been arrested! Taken to the police station! Questioned!'

He gulped down some mineral water.

'When she was released, I really gave her a rocket, I can tell you. I asked her what on earth it was all about! Was it something to do with a Godforsaken "rave" with horrible loud music and flashing lights? How often have I implored her to come to one of our alpha meetings at Holy Trinity

Brompton instead. "Perhaps Gerald Ronson will play his guitar," I tell her. "It's always splendid fun, do come!" But no, she wants to "do her own thing". I know sometimes young people can get mixed up with a bad crowd, but one never thinks it's going to happen to one's own children. How in the name of God has it come to this? You're so lucky, Al, that your children have not made the headlines.'

Jonathan suddenly became eerily calm. 'I asked her to pray with me, Al. I asked her to kneel with me and I would pray that she be forgiven. She just snorted and stalked out.'

What a dark night of the soul this is.

House of Commons   *Tuesday, 17 March*

I was on my way to the House this morning to hear the Chancellor's dull and vapid Budget when my mobile went and I heard Jonathan calling from what appeared to be a tiny cell.

'Now they've arrested *me*, Al!' he cried. 'What in the name of God is going on?'

But presently he regained his calm and the imprisoned John Bunyan could not have been more pious. He has need of these inner resources, because apparently Jonathan's unspeakable wife is in Tibet at the moment, humming and floating cross-legged three inches above the ground in Lhasa in flowing orange robes, so she is not in a position to offer much emotional support.

'They are fools, Al,' he said. 'The questioning of fools is as the crackling of thorns under a pot. They may beat me, and torture me; they may grind me beneath their polished Metropolitan Police boots, but I shall forgive them, for

they know no better. I say unto them that verily they are
the unwashed and unlearned, and that they are unclean and
eaters of broken meats! The fools ask me questions about
something I am supposed to have done last year. But I
simply laugh and say, "Do ye not know, ye fools? The time
has come to look forward!" Then I sang "Lord of the
Dance" until they allowed me this phone call.'

I asked Jonathan if he was aware that Mr Said Ayas, the
Saudi aide, had also been arrested.

There was a terrible silence from his end. Then, 'Al, get
my solicitor on the phone, could you?' he snapped, his
serenity suddenly under strain.

Saltwood   *Sunday, 22 March*

Thank God I did not reply to that letter I received last
month from Mr Paul Burrell, the late Princess's 'butler'.
(Did she have an *extensive* domestic staff?) He accompanied
his note with a photograph of his own seraphically smiling
face and the message:

Dear Alan,
D would have loved you to come to the Hollywood Diana Ball in
LA – and I should know. I was her 'rock', although I don't like
to talk about these intensely private things. She often talked about
the day last May when she voted for you: she often confided about
how she didn't like those creepy New Labour sales assistants and
counter-jumper types and wanted a proper Conservative Member.
She felt that you and she were on the same wavelength. May I put
you down for a table at £5,000? It would be so lovely to see you
there. I have put you and Jane next to Mr and Mrs Steven

Spielberg and Mr and Mrs Tom Cruise.

Love,
Paul

PS. Please don't talk to everyone about the fact that I was her 'rock'. It is an intensely private thing.

As I understand it, not a single one of these Hollywood stars has turned out for Mr Burrell's media offensive, leaving him with Mr and Mrs Rod Stewart, Ms Jane Seymour of the popular television programme *Dr Quinn, Medicine Woman*, Mr and Mrs Jerry Springer,[1] Mr and Mrs Gary Kemp[2] and Mr Lennox Lewis and his sainted mother – all of whom are offered the chance to pose for photographers with Paul, the late Princess's representative on earth.

A subsequent engagement never looked more necessary.

House of Commons   *Tuesday, 24 March*

The House is murmuring about the fact that the Right Honourable Member for Huntingdon has condemned the exploitative Diana industry, and its effect on the 'boys'.

What a curious figure little Major cuts now. So often in the corridors or in the chamber I see his resentful face with its oddly pursed upper lip, and hair bleached white with

---

[1] Jerry Springer is presenter of the American television programme
  The Jerry Springer Show.
[2] Gary Kemp is a former member of the popular ensemble Spandau
  Ballet.

past cares. It takes a physical effort of will to remember that
he came between the Lady and Blair. He is the Lord
Liverpool of modern times – the forgotten Premier.

I remember seeing him last week at Pratt's, dining with
Andrew Devonshire, and I have never seen anyone look so
ill at ease, always bobbing up in his seat, trying to greet
people who seemed to look straight through him. He
lurched nervously up on seeing me, causing a great clash of
crockery and knives, and stammered, 'Ah, Alan, I . . .' But
I'm afraid I swept past – somehow I could not face a
conversation with Major; it is too great a spiritual expense.
The last thing I remember was seeing him eat what
appeared to be an entire artichoke with a knife and fork
while Andrew gazed incuriously up at a corner of the
ceiling.

House of Commons   *Wednesday, 25 March*

Apparently unscathed by his brush with the police,
Jonathan is very exercised about the new Anthrax scare that
the Government is busily putting about to keep us all
focused and 'on message' about what a visionary and
courageous Leader we have.

'It's terrible news, Al,' he hissed, over luncheon.
'Terrible. That sort of publicity is highly injurious!'

Jonathan takes an abiding interest in the product of
Anthrax Surprise, a Black Country firm (est. 1981) which
has long been a purveyor of fatal spores to the Middle East.
Saddam is one of their most valued customers, sometimes
coming over here incognito for a few days and staying at
the local Travelodge. If the Government is unsportingly

cracking down on their retail opportunities in this way, it might have a very deleterious effect on the firm's future turnover.

'This could cost 250 jobs in Dudley, Al!' moaned Jonathan, tasting a decent Chablis without relish. 'If you could see the workmanship those chaps put in at the laboratory, it would break your heart. Why on earth is Blair giving out these irresponsible, sensational stories to the newspapers?'

Albany   *Thursday, 26 March*

Emerging from the Connaught after dinner, I felt a tugging at my trouser-leg and heard a strange squeaky voice coming from somewhere at knee level.

I looked down and saw an extraordinary figure with longish hair and a spherical pink face, wearing a lime-green corduroy suit with a long scarf. I vaguely recognised him as the author of *The Phantom of the Opera*, and a number of other musicals in the West End that bring in the Prestatyn coach parties by the thousand: Lord Lloyd-Webber. He is one of those public figures who we had very greatly feared would leave the country after the Great May Uprising.

'How did you enjoy your meal?' he squeaked.

Impertinent. But I gave him my opinion anyway, and he nodded thoughtfully. He went on to say that he is the regular restaurant reviewer for the *Telegraph*, but for the next month he is going to be away, superintending a massive new tour of *Jonah Man Jazz* throughout the Far East, and he needs someone to fill in for him.

'Obviously, there is only one man with the kind of

taste, distinction and sheer style who could do it.'

I began to preen. 'Well, Andrew, I –'

'But Matthew Freud wasn't available. God knows, we begged him. I can't tell you how often I have telephoned him and said, "Matthew, for God's sake, help me out here!" But it was no can do. And then Ainsley Harriott dropped out. But anyway, Alan, what do you say?'

Despite a considerable *froideur*, I agreed, on the strict understanding that I would not have to eat any meat.

'Yes, yes, fine,' said Andrew vaguely, and then jumped into my taxi.

Really.

House of Commons   *Friday, 27 March*

Here in the House, there is still a good deal of loose talk about the fact that, while the Budget debate was going on in the Chamber, I was espied out on the Terrace with Fr Michael Seed. I will make no apology for this. There is more truth in what that saintly man has to say than in the Chancellor's intellectually vapid nonsense.

We paced together by the glittering river, discussing transubstantiation, and David Starkey's new television programme about Henry VIII, the mention of whom caused Fr Michael's brow to furrow darkly.

Eventually, he asked, 'Would you like to borrow that copy of Thomas à Kempis I was talking about the other morning?'

I readily agreed, but just as he produced the slim quarto volume, Miss Ann Widdecombe appeared as if from nowhere and snatched it from my hand. 'I think, Father, you promised that to me,' she said tartly and marched off. Fr Michael forestalled my protests with a look of otherworldly mildness.

Once again, Ms Widdecombe takes precedence because of the Great Divide. How much longer can I maintain this contradiction?

Albany   *Monday, 30 March*

Ran into Malcolm [Rifkind] this afternoon. He is seething over our Foreign Secretary's nuptials at Chevening.

'Look at them, Alan,' he moaned, pointing at a photograph of Robin and Gaynor, who, consciously or not, had modelled their stomach-turning photo-call on Charles and Diana's first appearance for the cameras. The most disturbing thing was that Gaynor was smiling: perhaps we should send a print overseas to scare Mr Netanyahu into submission. Presumably Robin and Gaynor then danced barefoot on the lawn for the photographers, in a very transport of love.

Meanwhile, I am astonished that the Prime Minister has lent his weight to something called the 'Free Deirdre' campaign. I assume this pusillanimous nonsense is inspired by the Northern Ireland Office and Mo Mowlam has persuaded Downing Street to get involved. Perhaps the Home Secretary will claim that imprisonment will be injurious to Deirdre's mental health, and she will be released to claim thousands of pounds of taxpayers' money in compensation. The most obvious criminals will be appeased in the service of the 'peace' process. It is quite obvious to me that this woman is guilty. The lenses of those ridiculous large glasses have clearly borne the red reflection of a recent bomb blast.

And yet something in that 'frightened' expression she puts on for the Press touches my heart. Perhaps if she were to try contact lenses and experiment with some nicer earrings, she might be rather presentable. In fact, Deirdre's scared yet pert expression is rather attractive – like Ulrike Meinhof's.

I have faxed the Northern Ireland Office to ask if a visit could be arranged, but no reply as yet. I shall keep trying.

House of Commons, afternoon   *Tuesday, 31 March*

Lunching today with Nick in the House, we were interrupted by a strange figure, trembling, wraith-like. With a start, I saw that it was my friend Ali,[1] a shadow of his former self.

He was clearly shaken by the roasting he has taken over the fact that he all but denied that little Blair telephoned Romano Prodi – the shifty-eyed man in a suit who presides over the brawling collection of Calabrian snakeskin shoe salesmen which the Italians laughingly call their 'government' – hoping to sell him Rupert Murdoch's package of soft-porn cable television channels.

Ali's handsome face was contorted in a terrible grimace; he was stooping; his eyes were red and he was making a piteous mewing sound like an injured kitten.

I excused myself from the table and we repaired to a

---

[1] Alastair Campbell, Downing Street Press Secretary and close friend of the Clarks.

discreet corner. Ali was sweating and stammering and snivelling so much that I had to slap him. He gave a great yelp and and cradled his cheek, pouting, but at least he was quiet after that.

'Get a *grip*, Ali!' I hissed as he rubbed his cheek, sniffing. 'Remember you're a Caius man. For goodness' sake what's the matter with you?'

'It's all this Prodi business,' he mumbled. 'It's getting to me. And . . . Tony was a bit cool to me this morning.'

'Look,' I said, 'if it'll help, I'll write something in one of the filthy papers tomorrow supporting you. How's that?'

Instantly, he brightened. 'That's great, Al!' he cried cheerfully. 'You're a brick! Are you and Jane still on for Friday?'

He strolled away, whistling 'Scotland The Brave'.

Thoughtfully, I returned to my table, to find Nick in an increasingly convivial and exuberant mood.

'Explain something to me, would you, Al?' he roared in a voice loud enough to make my spleen vibrate, and jabbing his plate with his fork. 'Be so good as to put me in the picture about something. What is this frightful muck?'

I opined mildly that it was ratatouille.

'Tastes like bloody rat's droppings. Argh!' He lurched unsteadily to his feet. 'Right. I am going into the Chamber now to speak on . . . regional aid!'

I asked delicately if he was all right.

'Of course I am all right,' he shouted. 'By God, I have never felt better in all my life. I shall now enliven the proceedings with some real debate!'

He marched purposefully away out of sight, returned with a Commons servant pointing the way to the Chamber, then strode off in the opposite direction.

Albany   *Thursday, 2 April*

The Lord Lloyd-Webber is preoccupied with super-intending his enormous 50th Birthday rally at the Albert Hall – so he informs me I still have to write his wretched restaurant column for the *Daily Telegraph*.

Today I went to Quaglino's in St James's, a cavernous place with an enormous staircase, full of visitors from Canvey Island and Billericay. My companions and I had an extremely pleasant lunch and afterwards I was diverted by the curious, bulky Q-shaped ashtray, which I picked up and weighed experimentally in one hand.

Suddenly I felt a diminutive waiter lay his hand firmly on my arm. 'Pleez, sair. Do *neurt* embarrass yourself. Zey are on sale by the bar.'

I pointed out to him in four pithy sentences that I would not allow such an object to be employed as a hamsters' pissoir at Saltwood, and departed vowing that I should never grace the place again. Where does a gentleman go to take nourishment among his own kind these days?

Albany   *Friday, 3 April*

I ran into Tom [King] at the Connaught this evening, and after some guarded raillery we agreed that this Government's defence policy is an embarrassing catastrophe.

He told me that their strange new Procurement Minister, Lord Gilbert, caused consternation in Malaysia by turning down an official Rolls-Royce with motorcycle outriders and then hiring some vulgar custard-yellow open-top sports-car with a horn that played 'La Cucaracha'. Extraordinary.

We are enchanted by the Court Martial of Forbidden Love, and were chortling over the pictures of the siren involved, Lt-Cdr Pearce, who has toyed with the affections of the poor booby Lt-Col Keith Pople, when my laughter died in my throat, and the backs of my hands prickled with shock and recognition.

'Oh my God,' I breathed, *sotto voce*. 'Karen!'

It was in 1989, while I was at Defence, and being shown round an aircraft carrier at Plymouth by a pert young Wren in a charmingly trim uniform. Karen. I adored the submissive yet provocative way she called me 'Minister' and led me around the craft.

In a *sportif* mood, I asked if she experienced any tensions or privations 'aboard ship'. A way could always be found, said the entrancing little minx, and led me skippingly down to her private quarters where I was hoping to give her a thorough explanation of 'Options for Change'. We made desultory conversation at first, and Karen smiled enigmatically while a procession of whining officers scratched fruitlessly at her door outside, begging for admission. Finally, the deafening sound of jump-jets started up, and Karen indicated that the discussion could properly commence.

Ah, a life on the ocean wave . . .

Saltwood   *Saturday, 4 April*

I am supposed to be taking part in a new BBC 'pilot' radio programme tomorrow with that bespectacled fellow Ian

Hargreaves, who has resigned his job as editor of the *New Statesman*, Geoffrey Robinson's intellectual flagship of the New Labour-supporting classes, to spend more time with his family. But I'm not sure I can face it. The programme is evidently part of John Birt's Great New Dawn at Radio 4 in which *Sailing By* and *North Utsira, South Utsira* are to be replaced by a panel of career burglars debating the relative merits of various Class-A drugs under the chairmanship of Michael Ignatieff. Frankly, the journey to Portland Place and Broadcasting House does not promise to be congenial.

Albany   *Tuesday, 7 April*

Since the New Year, I have kept my campaign for the London mayoralty on a low light, but clearly I do have to make sure that all sections, all communities, are adequately 'consulted' – to use the current spasmoid phrase. This is why Jane and I attended a reception tonight in Maiden Lane given by an organisation called 'GAL-Lon' – the gay and lesbian campaign to elect a Mayor who is suitably friendly to their issues.

As the Member for Kensington and Chelsea, I feel that this is not a constituency which it is wise to ignore entirely. So we attended and mingled with various young men and women sporting a great deal of cold steel in their faces, and I applauded loudly whenever there was a speech. Furthermore, I took an interest in a magazine called *Skin Two*, in which the needs and aspirations of this community were given a very full airing.

But I was astonished to see that well-known friend of

London politics Steven Norris[1] at the event, whose character he did not seem to have fully grasped. He kept chatting animatedly to the brightly dressed young women present, but always turning dispiritedly away at the last.

'I'm not making any headway, Al,' he murmured.

Jane and I exchanged glances.

Saltwood   *Sunday, 12 April*

I had hoped to enjoy the peace and tranquillity of this holy day here in quiet contemplation. Instead, our proprieties have been 'challenged' by a co-ordinated attack from the gay rights movement. While George Carey, with wholly typical Anglican pusillanimity, allows Peter Tatchell to storm the Canterbury pulpit, the Greek pop singer George Michael has chosen a Beverly Hills lavatory as the venue in which to declare his opposition to homophobia. He has been arrested committing a homosexual act on his own. How does that work, exactly?

Completely absurd, of course, but the news about Michael nevertheless caused very great dismay to Ali and Fiona[2] who have been up here for the weekend.

'Jesus, Al!' he barked, fretting over his laptop, which is connected via a modem to Excalibur, the central Millbank computer. 'Have we invited him to Downing Street? I'm sure Peter set up a photo-op at some stage; when the hell

---

[1] Conservative MP for Oxford East 1983–7, Epping Forest 1988–97; former junior Transport Minister; now Director-General of the Road Haulage Association.

[2] Alastair Campbell's partner.

was it? Francis Maude is going to crucify us for this. Oh
Christ, why couldn't we have stuck with Ian McKellen?'

But it turns out that Mr Michael has never lent his
considerable prestige to the New Labour 'project',
preferring to remain barricaded in his mansion in Radlett
or Welwyn Garden City, the electrified gates swinging
open only to admit the monthly delivery of oranges.

Jane and I are more concerned with our forthcoming
'champagne garden party' in July for the Constituency
Party's mutinous and perpetually complaining stalwarts – a
truly horrific event that I have been bullied into organising
here at Saltwood. Apparently, if nothing of the sort is laid
on, other ranks at K&C will kick up, and all manner of
voluntary administrative and secretarial services might be
withdrawn. Thankfully, one of our Gauleiters has managed
to obtain for them about 10 crates of Pomagne, the tasty
champagne perry cordial, from an off-licence in Notting
Hill Gate, and I will not need to deplete our stock of Dom
Perignon.

The charge will be £20 per head, cash or cheque (Visa
and Mastercard not acceptable). Coaches will park outside
and their occupants will be chivvied smartly through the
gates, at which a Party official will check that their
invitations are authentic. From there, they will be taken
through into the gardens (no matter if the weather is
inclement), there to mingle and listen to my brief but
uplifting speech thanking them for their hard work. A small
Portaloo will be available, as guests will on no account be
allowed to enter the main house – and to ensure
compliance I shall tell the rabble that Hanna, Leni and Eva
will be kept hungry and untied for the whole afternoon.
Coaches will ferry them back at about 4.30 p.m.

With luck, the whole dire event should be over in a
few hours.

Saltwood *Monday, 13 April*

I am seventy. Frankly, I cannot believe it. I will not believe it.

When I look in the mirror. I see a man of perhaps 52 or 53. My musculature is taut; I have put on no extra weight. I can swim the moat without difficulty, and I can run a hundred-yard dash with only a few rest-breaks. Unclothed, I have a distinctively *Roman* aspect, an attribute which I am tempted to display to passers-by here at Saltwood, but Jane has dissuaded me. Perhaps she is right. There is no point in fomenting envy and discontent among the younger men locally.

I can still turn female heads when in town, especially when I fix them with my devastatingly candid gaze, part seduction, part challenge. It is quite irresistible, especially when I accompany it with my taunting smile and perhaps a few words of greeting, hinting intriguingly at an intimate encounter. I did it in Piccadilly the other day with a rather amusing young woman. She pouted adorably, visibly unsettled by the turbulent emotions I was arousing in her. Clearly, the veneer of politeness was wafer-thin.

Who knows how many encounters a man must *pass over* in his life, unexplored, like novels unwritten, symphonies uncomposed, or indeed Cabinet posts unfilled?

House of Commons *Tuesday, 14 April*

There is such a danger in coming into the Commons these days; one is liable to be waylaid by all manner of extraordinary types. Major, of all people, loomed up in front of me in the Tea Room, gulping and clearing his throat, his Adam's apple bobbing up and down.

'Ah, Alan, I wonder if I could have a word about Ken?'

As I feared, our former Prime Minister is busying himself with his infinitely tiresome new hobby: trying to promote the puff-ball Kenneth Clarke back into the Shadow Cabinet because Major feels the corpulent former Chancellor is 'wasted' on the back benches – although how exactly this concerns Major now is a mystery to us all, particularly to our new young Leader, who feels the back benches are exactly the right place for both these architects of catastrophe.

I fear Major will inevitably tread the Lady's undignified path to bitter obscurity.

House of Commons   *Wednesday, 15 April*

I am captivated by the news of the 51-year-old Governor of the Falkland Islands, Richard Ralph, and his liaison with Miss Jemma Jackson. At 25, Miss Jackson is perhaps a little old to be really succulent but one must nevertheless salute Mr Ralph's vigour. His plumes of office have evidently given him a peacock virility. Mrs Ralph was evidently rash enough to return home to Lancashire, leaving Richard to cultivate his *amour fou* in that desolate and freezing outpost of penguins, where a few mangy and unkempt sheep occasionally stray bleating on to the grim beach, there to be blown sky-high by undiscovered landmines.

And yet – really, the age issue is a problem and they will have to confront it sooner or later. In 10 years' time, Jemma will be 35, and Ralph will begin to cast about for someone younger.

It is the way of the world.

Albany   *Friday, 17 April*

I am extremely chagrined that one Anthony O'Hear – a chippy academic with the bow tie, frizzy hair, and pinched expression of the habitual *frotteur* – has had the temerity and the sheer bad taste to criticise Princess Diana. The substantive charges, as I am given to understand, are that she had no concept of 'duty' and that she encouraged inauthentic sentimentality in the nation.

Perhaps this loathsome 'pundit' would care to furnish one single concrete example of Diana neglecting her Royal duty – neglecting it, that is, before she had been expelled from the Royal Family and her name removed from the list of Family members to be prayed for.

Diana was nothing less than a goddess. When I think of her blonde beauty and that lovely off-centre smile, it is all I can do to stop myself sobbing. I have already recorded in this journal my last meeting with her on 30 April last year. I shall never forget it. I had landed my helicopter on the lawn of Kensington Palace. As the blades' rotation slowed, in the fighting man's crouching run I boldly approached the sunbed on which she was reclining in that exquisitely languorous, youthful way. We then entered her private apartments for a brief discussion of matters European; suffice it to say, she made it *absolutely* clear that she would be supporting me. It makes my blood boil when Blair claims her as some kind of New Labour 'People's Princess'

when, as everyone knows, her last political act was to vote
Conservative.

Chelsea Town Hall   *Tuesday, 21 April*

Today I was forced to sit through a curious public meeting
at Chelsea Town Hall, the purpose of which was to
reiterate our profound belief that Chelsea's position as the
international epicentre of Swinging Britain should be
indefinitely preserved – presumably with Lottery cash –
despite the fact that the whole 'swinging' thing was as
bogus 30 years ago as it is now.

Stephen Bayley, who has been brutally sacked by
Mandelson as the designer of the exhibition in the
ruinously expensive Millennium Dome, wittered on about
the need for 'fewer cars, fewer formulaic stores, fewer bad
restaurants' – for all the world as if the design catastrophe of
the Nineties had nothing to do with him.

Mary Quant was there, droning on about how
wonderful 'Terence' is. Really, it is a miracle how Conran
has preserved his position in British public life. I said, 'The
wealth and the quality and the people and the whole gifted
entity that surrounds us here in Chelsea remind me of some
wonderful Greek city state that has everything at its disposal
should it need to aspire to a higher level of independence.'
As ever, with the maturer constituents of Kensington and
Chelsea, I *sparkled.* I had the audience in the palm of my
hand.

I suppose I have a sentimental attachment to the King's
Road. Many's the time I have cruised up and down its
reaches on a sunlit Saturday afternoon in the SS 100, on the

lookout for a likely cultural encounter. How often have I seen some young Bohemian person outside some coffee bar, really very similar to the women speaking on the panel with me: Vikki Heywood, the executive director of the Royal Court, or the lovely aquiline dark-haired sculptress Marzia Colonna.

Marzia is fascinating. I sauntered up to her, intending to inquire if she wished to repair to some discreet venue to discuss local Chelsea politics.

'Alan!' she said as I approached. 'Do you want to sit down?' She jumped up from her seat. Somehow, I found my desire to discuss Chelsea receding.

House of Commons   *Wednesday, 22 April*

The first anniversary of the Blair reign approaches, and our side has never looked more utterly abject and defeated. Really, it would be less embarrassing to be one of Paddy's Lib-Dem troops in open-toed sandals, talking about single transferable votes and smoking marijuana. God, this is so humiliating.

The final straw was little Mackay,[1] our supposed Ulster spokesman. He has been on some package holiday in Namibia with Julie Kirkbride (he does not deserve her) when he should be keeping our end up as Blair proposes to sell the United Kingdom down the river to SDLP/Sinn Fein/IRA because there is simply no one to oppose him, except the *Daily Telegraph*.

I tried redressing the balance today during Prime

---

[1] Andrew Mackay, Conservative MP for Bracknell since 1997.

Minister's Questions, asking when the Government is
going to show to two British Guardsmen currently held in
prison the same clemency that they have shown to the
various gloating and unrepentant terrorists. He favoured
me with some waffle about 'consideration' given to the
matter. When are we going to see some leadership on our
benches? Looking at little Hague's plump and vacuous face,
concerned with the all-important 'Policy Review', I feel a
terrible, nauseous anger.

House of Commons   *Monday, 27 April*

In the Commons now, one year after the Great Débâcle,
the Conservative ranks have never looked more defeated
and emasculated: like the conscripts of a conquered army
forced to parade before their captors in unlaced boots.

And no matter what we say, what we do, the papers are
like Moonies, praising Blair without any capacity for
rational thought – even under the Lady, we never had this
much zombie support.

In the Tea Room today, I was approached by someone
who I thought might be a minor civil servant, or possibly
even the junior manager at the local Abbey National. It
turned out to be young Stephen Dorrell,[1] who took me
aside and said gravely, 'Alan, I am resigning from the
shadow Cabinet.'

So what? Who on earth is even going to *notice*? Who

---

[1] Conservative MP for Loughborough 1979–97, Charnwood since
    1997; former Financial Secretary to the Treasury; former National
    Heritage Secretary.

cares about the spastic 'shadow Cabinet', a group of men whose deliberations are so irrelevant that they might as well be conducted on Pluto?

Albany   *Tuesday, 28 April*

I have decided that my candidature for the London mayoralty – an amiable idea in which I indulged briefly over the New Year period – will have to be abandoned. Having briefly considered Ken, I have now decided to throw my support behind Jeffrey Archer: a man whose intellectual capacity and integrity exactly match the status and importance of this newly created role in public life. Jeffrey was so overcome when I told him that he almost blubbed.

Earlier this evening, we were in his flat – or 'penthouse' as he insists on calling it – surrounded by review copies of his latest work of prose fiction. Jeffrey put his full tumbler down on one of the piles, strode across, tremblingly grasped my hand in both of his, and almost broke down.

'Alan, I can't tell you how much your support means to me,' he said in a hoarse whisper. 'With your help, I shall clinch the Conservative nomination and get the job! And I guarantee that you will have a strong chance of being Deputy Mayor, though obviously I can't promise anything. Now if you'll excuse me, I have to preside over an important charity auction.'

I am looking forward to getting away for the Bank Holiday. What a wonderful year it has been back in Westminster, with some stunning victories, reminding the public and the Party what a real political leader looks like.

Now I think I shall keep this Diary private for the time being, publishing them only when the need arises.

But through the mists I can foresee a future time — a time when our forces are being taken off the beaches in small boats, a time when the Conservative Party, and indeed Britain itself, will cry out in its darkest hour for a man of destiny to emerge from his Kentish castle and pull the sword from the stone.

I shall be ready.

Appendix

Not ⋀Alan Clark's Favourite Things

Favourite Women in Politics

The Lady
Perhaps rather an obvious one, this. One feels about the Lady the way one might feel about one's first love – obviously one will always feel strongly about her, not merely personally, but politically. (What was Burke's line about a thousand swords leaping from their scabbards to protect Marie-Antoinette, the adorable *Autrichienne*? Did he realise quite how *sexual* that was?) But when all is said and done, feeling abject rapture in the Lady's presence seems a little quaint now; all that I feel is nostalgia. But still.

Golda Meir
A powerful woman. Something in that heavy jowl, the dark skin, the residual hint of a *beard*. Compelling.

Sara Netanyahu
Now here is a woman on the international stage who *really* commands attention. Whether she has had cosmetic surgery on her nose is a moot point. I have decided, after some deliberation, that I am unconcerned about this matter. I admire very much the way she treats her domestic staff. Any nonsense from the nannies, or the below-stairs personnel, and out they go. It all goes to show: servants are like lovers: if you want to keep them, you must treat them badly.

Perhaps the most entrancing thing about Sara is that she used to be an *air hostess*. Many is the time, during a dull

Debate in the House, I have rested my eyes, and lost myself
in a delicious reverie. I am on a flight to Tel Aviv; I press
the button to call the stewardess, and Sara appears with an
ambiguous smile – we have already exchanged some
charged badinage about stowing my 'package', and
whether or not she could handle my 'equipment'. I
twinklingly request a blanket; she brings it and then
snuggles beneath it with me and we discuss the Oslo
Agreement in truly *intime* surroundings.

Ffion Jenkins
Or Mrs Ffion Hague, as I suppose we must now think of
her. But Ffion has a secret. I am convinced of it. And it is
this. Her marriage has not been consummated. I am certain
of it. On a number of occasions, she has caught my eye
with a troubled yet yearning look, a sensitive, delicate soul
whose *expectations* have not been met. She is like Dorothea,
in the clutches of an absurd Casaubon. At a Conservative
Party reception recently, she smiled faintly at me, and I am
certain that her fingertips brushed mine, discreetly,
imploringly.

Clare Short
Simply the most wonderful woman in the modern Labour
Party. There is no one else who comes close (with the
exception of Claire Ward, a brilliant and talented young
woman who is Government material, surely?). When Clare
and I finally had dinner it was absolutely sublime. I took her
to the Halcyon, and all evening we gazed into each other's
eyes and we laughed, oh, how we laughed! Clare was on
excellent form about state help for Sudan; I leaned forward
and murmured something about how we were on *exactly*
the same wavelength on this one, trade not aid, buying
their coffee and so on. Sadly, in reaching across to whisper

my policy position in her ear, I knocked over a glass of the Surançon and the moment was rather spoiled.

❦

Favourite 'Cool Britannia' Style Icons

Pulp
Obviously Mr Jarvis Cocker would have his work cut out to pass muster on any Conservative candidates' shortlist; there is something in the way his hair is perpetually uncombed and the way the bottom buttons of his shirt are undone, revealing a noisome length of flesh, that would turn most Constituency Associations against him. (However, he might do to contest an East London seat, see if he dents their majority, then perhaps let him have a crack at somewhere in the Midlands in 2007?) The reason I am thinking out loud in this way is that Mr Cocker is so clearly on the Conservative side; Blair would *loathe* him. Many is the time that I have surveyed the Government benches and whistled 'Common People' under my breath. Very catchy. And I particularly like the cover of their new album, *This Is Hardcore*, featuring a young blonde woman who reminds me of a *very* fetching research assistant I used to have. The photograph only shows her face, but she is in some sort of supine position, and someone is doing to her what Labour is doing to the economy.

Damien Hirst
There is something so *deracinated* in that C2 face that I cannot help but be amused by Mr Hirst. That expression of contempt, combined with sub-human belligerence, is intriguing – worn chiefly when he has just sold some blob of red paint or dismembered knacker's-yard reject to Charles Saatchi for £750,000. With his low, sniggering

cunning, he looks like one of those other-ranks sort of
chaps who managed to get out of National Service by
staying up all night before the medical examination
drinking brandy and smoking cigars. The other evening I
found myself having an informal policy consultation in
Notting Hill, and an urgent situation had arisen. I had need
of certain supplies and I darted into what I thought was a
pharmacy. Imagine my chagrin when I discovered it was
one of Mr Hirst's absurd restaurants. Really.

Chris Smith

No one exemplifies the thrillingly alive, creative, outward-
looking young country that is the New Britain more than
this middle-aged bespectacled bachelor, who has recently
written in his seminal text, *Creative Britain*, that 'Jazzy B'
and 'Roni Size' have really put black music on the map. It
is a profound privilege to be serving in a Parliament which
has Government politicians of this calibre.

Alexander McQueen

The name seems correct for a designer, but really, does Mr
McQueen *look* the part? Shouldn't he look like a haggard
Frenchman wearing heavy spectacles and a mauve jacket
over his shoulders, surrounded by excitable young women.
Mr McQueen looks like one of those overweight young
men who accost one in Soho, inquire if one needs a mini-
cab, and then ask if there is *anything else* one requires. He
has evidently designed a pair of trousers which are properly
worn so that the cleavage of one's buttocks is prominent. I
have suggested to Nick Soames that he tries sporting a pair
to give the Conservative Party some much-needed
credibility in the New Britain.

Favourite Footballers

Paul Gascoigne
I'm afraid that, though I am amused by Mr Gascoigne, I cannot condone his obsession with feeding his face at every available opportunity. I myself take luncheon extremely sparingly, and I have been rewarded with a physique on which there is not a trace of fat.

Julian Dicks
Really, one cannot help but adore a footballer who always looks so candidly *brutish*, so very obviously ready to get 'stuck in'. That shaven head reminds me of some of the bravest, most stout-hearted men who fought in the trenches in the First World War. Nowadays, we do not have wars, so our young men with Mr Dicks's energy and talents must channel them into making the odd late tackle. A bit of a *clogger*, to use the amusing argot of the terraces.

Tony Adams
There is something of working-class pathos, even tragedy, in that gaunt expression and colossal nose. I can well imagine that face a mask of anguish and pain, as the cell door shut every night with a tremendous clang, and Mr Adams was left to contemplate an existence without alcoholic refreshment of any kind. I think Ibsen might have found inspiration in Mr Adams's drawn and haggard countenance. Put Mr Adams in a frock-coat and he would make an excellent nineteenth-century Norwegian lawyer in the grip of some awful ethical dilemma.

Jürgen Klinsmann
One naturally admires the Germans above all players. They have the fortitude, the courage, and the martial intelligence

of the Wehrmacht on the Russian front. I also admire the way Jürgen manipulates the referee's emotions with complaints and harmless play-acting. Germany used to do something very similar with the League of Nations.

Favourite Restaurants

Wiltons
Of course, this is really the *only* restaurant I can include in this category. It serves the exact antithesis of all the emetic 'Modern British' cuisine foisted off on us by the new restaurants where one is waited on by young women. The rule is: the more men there are waiting on one, the more acceptable the establishment is. Wiltons tends, however, to be replete with people from school, who tend to greet one very noisily on the way in, making it quite hopeless for discreet meetings.

Favourite Cartoon Characters

Deputy Dawg
This absurd dog, entrusted with some position of police power, intrigues and exasperates me at the same time. Who exactly is the wretched beast deputy *to*? He typifies a sort of Jobsworth socialism, insistent on his stifling rules and regulations, and exactly the sort of policeman I loathe. He is also very prone to mixing with his preposterous cronies, such as the egregrious 'Musk Rat'. But as with some particularly long-serving retainer, one can't help but be charmed by him.

Penelope Pitstop

Penelope is a spirited girl: there is something about a beautiful young woman behind the wheel of a fast car that I find absolutely *delicious*. Her clothes are also rather diverting. There is something at once assertive and yielding about Penelope: like the very best sort of female civil servant. I like to think that when Penelope calls out, 'Hay-elp! Hay-elp!' I will be on hand to give assistance.

Barney Rubble

My general rule is: *never* trust a man with blond hair. It is almost certainly dyed, indicating some sort of aberrant sexual practice. But I am prepared to suspend this convention in Barney's case. There is something so heartbreakingly bourgeois about him in his devotion both to his lady wife and to his friend and neighbour Fred. Barney is the salt of the earth.

Homer Simpson

As with 'Gazza', one deprecates Homer's habit of over-eating, but he is at any rate a trenchant defender of the private nuclear industry which has brought so much employment to the lower-middle classes.

Favourite Models

Sophie Dahl

See Homer Simpson and Gazza, above. Sophie is a charming girl, but when I took her to the Caprice, the conversation did not make much headway, beyond her asking for the sweet trolley all the time.

Kate Moss
An amusing girl, but really, she should keep her mouth closed as much as possible. That *accent*. Such a disappointment. I simply do not have the time to put in a Henry Higgins effort. However, with things the way they are, she might make a good platform speaker at Party conference. Perhaps I should make a note to mention this to Cecil.

Claudia Schiffer
Really, I can become quite embarrassingly enthusiastic about Claudia, who confided to me over dinner that she was terribly unhappy with that American conjuror Oliver Twist or A Tale of Two Cities or whatever his name is. In moments of animation or excitement, she speaks in the most wonderfully harsh German. Or she does with me anyway. Ravishing.

Cindy Crawford
As with Ffion, and indeed Claudia, one suspects that Miss Crawford has not really had the man that she deserves. Mr Richard Gere might be a splendid thespian, but one wonders if Cindy was entirely aware of his domestic habits before she formed an attachment to him? When we had dinner some years ago in Los Angeles, Cindy tearfully confessed that things were not all that they should be. It colours her work with a note of melancholy, in my opinion.

Favourite Films

Bambi
One cannot help but sympathise with the young deer who has to grow up in the wild after his mother is shot by hunters. As a vegetarian, I consider that this film makes the idea of venison more loathsome than ever. However, I must say that Bambi's so-called friends leave a little to be desired: Thumper is a complete *shit*.

The Bridge on the River Kwai
God, the *whining* of these people. Perhaps if they had put up a better show defending Singapore they wouldn't have got into this mess.

The Sound of Music
It is a pleasure to see a film that emphasises the essentially benign character of Austrians during the Second World War.

Chitty Chitty Bang Bang
I have always yearned for a car that actually takes flight. Once I took the SS 100 up to 201 mph and its front wheels left the ground for eleven seconds.

Reservoir Dogs
This reminded me *intensely* of the EC discussions of the Common Agricultural Policy I attended when I was at Trade. The scene in which the police officer has his ear cut off has something distinctively *communautaire* about it.

The Triumph of the Will
I have a soft spot for this, because it reminds me of *Carry On, Sergeant*.

About the Author

Peter Bradshaw was born in 1962 and was educated at Haberdashers' Aske's School, Elstree, and Pembroke College, Cambridge, where he was President of Footlights. He is a columnist for the London *Evening Standard* and has also written for *The Modern Review*, the *London Review of Books*, *Tribune*, the *Times Literary Supplement* and the *Independent on Sunday*.

Index

Adams, Gerry 109–10
  an invitation 98–99
Aitken, Jonathan 46–48
  arrested 165–66
  daughter arrested 164–65
  and a kilt 46–47
  little Hong Kong parcel 51
  and a sheep 48, 49
Anderson, Bruce 6, 13
Anthrax Surprise 153, 168
Armoured Personnel Carrier 47
Arms to Iraq xii
Ashdown, Paddy 62
astrolabes and ladies' underwear
    84

battle with Hastings and all that
    xvi–xix, 36, 41, 121–25
  cost of litigation 131
  final day 135
  victory! 137–38
  victory party 135–36
beef 118
Bell, Martin 14
  legal bill 143
  that suit 12
bin bags *See* ginger wigs *and*
    Cook, Robin
Birt, John
  Great New Dawn 176
  a shit 68
Blair, Cherie, and Humphrey's

  pee 113
Blair, Tony
  and the Lady 38
  People's Question Time 41
  PMQ Nouveau 61
  tobacco *mea culpa* 109
bonding session
  cock-up 83
  the purple sweatshirt 64
  the red sweatshirt 63
  three-line whip 96
  the yellow sweatshirt 63
Bradbury . . . Bradshaw, or
    whoever, Peter 15
  impassive in defeat 138
  impertinence 34
  legal battle begins 35–36
  not the GBH 26–27
  not the handcuffs 122
Brown, Gordon
  emergency budget 52
  shifty 135
Brown Monday 95

Campbell, Alastair, and the
    Italian job 172–73
Carey, George
  choice for Charles 66–67
  storming of the pulpit 177
Carlton, the – geriatric ward 100
Chirac, Jacques 39–40
chronology

1997 1–4
1998 129
Clark, Colin (brother)
    autobiography 82, 102–3
    fat 103
    and Priscilla 103
    and Libby Purves 105
Clarke, Arthur C. 144
Clinton, Bill 142–43
Conservative Party
    name change? 119
    torch extinguished 152
Cook, Robin
    and a black plastic rubbish
        sack 65
    and Gaynor Regan 65
    theme party 66
    wife dumps to *Times* 136–37
cuckolds and horsewhips 16

Defence Capabilities 'R' Us 86
devolution
    no, NO! campaign 80
    Scotland 79
    Wales 61
Diana Ball 166–67
Diana pizzas 81
Diana, Princess of Wales 25
    death of 75–77
    and Dodi Fayed 67
    funeral of 77–78
Diaries
    second volume? 148
    the spoof 15
Dome 50
    not the genitals 154

Ecclestone, Bernie 106–7

Blair's *mea culpa* 109
election victory 27
elephants, golden 74
ethical trade, absurdities of xii
Evening Standard prosecution *See*
    battle with Hastings and all
    that

favourite cartoon characters
    192–93
favourite Cool Britannia style
    icons 189–90
favourite films 195
favourite footballers 191–92
favourite models 193–94
favourite restaurants 192
favourite women in politics
    187–89
Fayed, Dodi, and Diana, Princess
    of Wales 67
field sports *See* foxhunting
Fitzsimmons, Lorna 94–95
floppy-toed clown shoes *See*
    Major *père*
Formula One 104
    Blair's *mea culpa* 109
foxhunting 44, 55–56
    Huntsmen's Nuremberg 56
    mass whinge-in 153
'Free Deirdre' campaign 171
'Free Speech for Dictators' 158
'Fresh Future Starts Now, The'
    83
Frost, Sir David: summer party
    48–49

George, Mr Boy 36
ginger wigs, beards and bin bags

See Cook, Robin
Goldsmith, James
  backgammon board, assault
    with 7–8
  dead 58–59
Goodlad, Alastair xiii, 21
Gorman, Teresa 45
Great Escape, the *See* Maze
  Prison
Gullet, Rod 152

Hague, Ffion *See* Jenkins, Ffion
Hague, William
  Brit pop three-line whip 149
  charisma bypass 55
  coconuts 74
  dumps Howard 29
  Hamley's mini-racing cars 106
  'Stonewall' rally 42
  Thatcher's backing 46
  wedding list 120
Hain, Peter: bank robbery 62
Hamilton, Archie 37
Hamilton, Neil 12
Händerhochschweinbühne 131
Hanna the Rottweiler 68–69,
  102
  and the Countryside March
    158–59
Harkess, James 16, 17
  forgiveness 18
Hastings, Max
  gloat 123
  knighthood recommendation
    41
  see also battle with Hastings
    and all that and *Evening*
    Standard

Heath, Sir Edward, and a
  disagreeable shock 30
Heseltine, Michael: leadership
  hopes 28
Hess, not Rudolph 38
History of the Conservative Party
  xvii, 58, 68, 78, 80
  BAFTA? 81
  Churchill downgraded 84–85
  'pro-Hitler' 88
home décor
  heavy automatic weapons xiv
  and Michael Winner 22
Hong Kong, surrender of 50–51
Howard, Michael
  auburn adulterer,
    denunciation of 146
  dumped by Hague 29
  'pipple' 42
  'something of the night' 31
Howe, Martin 5
Humphrey the cat
  and Rory Bremner 115
  pees on Cherie 113
Hurd, Douglas, and thrashing 85
Hutchence, Michael 112

Irvine, Lord (Derry): denuding
  the galleries 156

Jenkins, Ffion 45, 46
  marriage consummated? 188
  naked, on a lion 79
  wedding list 120
Jones, Paula 142–43

Kensington and Chelsea
  selection 7

Kensington ladies' under-
    garments 16
Kirkbride, Julie
    not the leather 106
    not the leather microskirt 97
    not the leather miniskirt 42

Labour Nouveau
    grins 10
    intake nouveau 30
Lady, the *See* Thatcher, Lady
    (Margaret)
leg irons 31
Leni the Rottweiler 101
Lewinsky, Monica 143
Lloyd-Webber, Lloyd: *Jonah
    Man Jazz* 169–70
Love Bus 64

maiden speech 40
Major, John xiii
    curious little figure 167–68
    leaving the stage 28–29
Major *père* and floppy-toed
    clown shoes 29
Mandelson, Peter
    Dome 50
    Parliamentary knowledge,
        extent of 30
    tears 35
    torture 69
Maude, Francis: Undermining-
    the-Millennium portfolio
    154
Mawhinney, Herr Doktor 10
    moat mishap 66
    quarrelsome 22
Mayhew, Lord (Patrick) 9

mayoralty
    Lord (Jeffrey) Archer 133, 185
    campaign begins 132
    candidature abandoned 185
    gay and lesbian campaign 176
    Chris Patten 132
    Peter Stringfellow 133
Maze Prison and the Great
    Escape 9
McGuinness, Martin 109–10
Mellor, David
    Lottery disaster 145
    urge to gloat 11
    urge to gloat again 27
Merchant, Piers 92–93
Michael, George: opposition to
    homophobia 177
Millennium Experience *See*
    Dome
Monserrat 73
MORI
    Goldsmith's apoplexy 8
    'plus' factor 11
motoring
    and a policeman's foot 83
    and Mr Toad xii, 82

New Labour *See* Labour
    Nouveau
Notting Hill Carnival 74
    an invitation 72–73
Parker Bowles, Camilla 44
    Soames's verdict 53
Patten, Chris
    and a brick 155
    juniper leaves and tigers
        132–33
Pearce, Edward 108

whingers' chrous 110
Persil *See* Bell, Martin
pipple 42, 146
Portillo, Michael 93
Powell, Enoch 148–49
     gone 148
Prescott, John
     Brit pop soaking 149
     housing deal 161
     and Peter the crab 71

Read, Pearl 145–46
Redwood, John: principles to
     the winds 46
Referendum Party 7–8
restaurant column 169, 174
Rifkind, Malcolm: Post-
     Traumatic-Shock
     Syndrome 118–19
Robinson, Geoffrey
     paltry £12 million stash 117
     pillorying 116–17

Saddam Hussein: Anthrax
     Surprise 168–69
Santer, Jacques 19
Saudis 85
'serial adulterer' gibe 27
seventieth birthday, but looking
     not a day over . . . 179
s**t 88
Short, Clare 59
     aid-to-trade seminar 60
     golden elephants 74
     Monserrat 73–74
     New Labour uniform 61
Sinn Fein 109
     de facto 'ceasefire' 60

Soames, Nicholas 53, 91–92
soufflé, the; gavel, the; and
     shoebox, the – and Emma
     100
Spencer, Earl: divorce 114
Summerson, Hugo 6

tarts' cards in telephone boxes
     160
Tatchell, Peter: storming of the
     pulpit 177
Tebbit, Lord (Norman) 16
     and multiculturalism 89
Teddy Bear Party 27
Thatcher, Lady (Margaret)
     aerobics on GMTV 22
     backing Hague 46
     Blair meeting 38
     Hong Kong handover 50
Toad, Mr xii, 82
Tory conference 1997 89–91
Tory leadership 41–42
     Hague's 'Stonewall' rally 42
     Heseltine's hopes 28
     Heseltine withdraws 29
     Howard's 'betrayal' 42
     Thatcher backs Hague 46
     wankers 33
Trelford, Donald 124

urinating fantasy xi

Waldegrave, William xiii, 93
Wales, Prince of
     and Archur C. Clarke 144
     divorce settlement 111
     and Camilla Parker Bowles 44
wankers *See* individual entries

Ward, Claire
    and an eye caught 33
    and a fluttering heart 36
    and a frostiness 44
    and a hanky 30
    and an invitation to lunch 107
Widdecombe, Ann
    chocolates and flowers 32

    Hello Dolly! 97
    neck–bolts 31
Windscale/Sellafield *See* Dome
Winner, Michael 22, 28
Wogga Wogga Association
    Football training camp 139
Wonderbras 145
Woodward, Louise 102